D0272365

COMING & CRYING

Edited by
Melissa Gira Grant and Meaghan O'Connell

"Some Thoughts on the Crapper" by Jonathan Ames was originally published in *Gawk*, 1997. "I Hit Her" by Alex Hoyt was originally published in *Filthy Gorgeous Things*, 2009.

Design by Jez Burrows

Published by Glass Houses Press
353 Third Avenue
Suite 105
New York, NY 10010
glasshousespress.com

ISBN-10: 0-61538-494-3
ISBN-13: 978-0-615-38494-8
Library of Congress Control Number: 2010909955

Printed in Iceland
First Edition
10 9 8 7 6 5 4 3 2 1

For you.

Contents

Introduction

This book started because we were writing each other stories, almost every day, before we had ever met. Neither of us was writing just for the other. We were writing for the Internet, for the Anyone that might be reading. Sometimes our stories were about sex, but sometimes they were about disappointment, bravery, being smaller or bigger than we imagined. Our storytelling emerged not out of a desire to make big claims about The Truth of Sex but from feeling how vital it was to report back. We said what we'd always been told were the worst things to say, the things not to say, and when we shared them, no one blinked. They seemed to need it, too. We asked each other for more.

So even in the very beginning we were not alone.

We knew from our earliest conversations that *Coming & Crying* was meant not to be *erotic* but *true*. We wanted to make a book that charged people with telling real stories about sex but didn't pressure them to turn anyone on. *Coming & Crying* aims not for conclusions about sex but for the truth that is found in our shared experience of it. We recognize each other as human not through a singular narrative, but in our own particular stories.

There are twenty-four stories in this book and we hope all of them will knock you out or wake you up or make you feel less alone. You'll encounter at least twenty-four people in a way one does not usually. Some of the names you'll recognize, because they are established writers or your friends or people you follow on the Internet already. That's how we know them, too.

These are stories told from the point at which we're at our most vulnerable. They have in common a rawness that might not emerge with the act of sex itself, but from a fear of seeing or feeling or saying too much. They may reveal a desire for all of that, too. There's love in the book and also the stark lack of it. There are beginnings—first kiss, first handjob, first sex tape, first rabies scare—and there are many more endings: some are sad, some bold. Most fall somewhere in the middle.

Coming & Crying is premised on an offering of self, a saying *Yes* when one of us asked. These stories are inseparable from our willingness to go there, our need to deliver something that isn't often told but that is essential to have in our hands as we make our way in the world with each other.

Meaghan and Melissa
Brooklyn, July 3, 2010

I Hit Her

Alex Hoyt

WE WERE ALREADY FUCKING. Her eyes were closed, and she was gathering the slack of the bedsheets into her hands. Maybe she was looking for purchase, a way to dig deeper into the bed, or maybe she just needed something to pull on as I pushed into her. As we started going harder, she reached for the rail of the headboard. Her hand found a piece of thick, square wood, slightly too big to hold. As she gripped, the edges of her fingers turned red, and the skin near the knuckles went white.

"Hit me," she said.

The frame was already barking. The bed was starting to shuffle away from the wall. I did what I thought she wanted and slapped her lightly across the face.

She turned her head into the mattress and spoke louder, not unhappily.

"*Hit* me. Harder. Hard."

I pulled back my hips and pulled back my hand. I slapped her as hard as I could. She made a noise, like crying but also like a hot intake of breath. She nodded. I did it again, a little less hard. I could see her face darkening and didn't want to leave a mark. My hand stung. I assumed her face hurt more. Watching her breathe harder and flex her legs to raise up her ass made my cock harder, quickly. We kept alternating—slap, inhale, fuck, slap, inhale, fuck—without talking. As we fucked increasingly hard, she made noises I didn't know. I took them as cues, so I would slap her as hard as I could, as hard as she seemed to want. There was no story running in my head. I was only reacting.

At one point, I swung too hard.

"Ouch," she said. She laughed. Her smile was the first acknowledgment that we were performing a ritual, finding a new way to perform for each other. "A little less," she said. "Do it." I hit her again three times, right at the border we'd found. I hadn't noticed it, but her hand was already on her clit. It had probably been there for several minutes. She scissored up suddenly, stopping our movement while she came.

Her torso flexed, and she couldn't really talk. "On me, on me" she said. It was familiar shorthand. I pulled out and came on her face, though most of the cum landed behind on the headboard. The experience had torqued me up, leaving my mouth dry. I had gone much further than I expected. She laughed, roomily, full of new air and old affection. She fell back onto the pillows and smiled.

She had pale skin, full of light and easily reddened. Her smile was always wide, even when she covered her teeth with her lips. Her hair was black and her eyes were a flinty, bright green. The colors alone could make me hard. She kissed with the rhythm of a practiced dance partner, never opening too wide or thrusting her tongue back too quickly. She was lying beneath me, cum flecking her left shoulder and her hair. Her stare was even and calm. We loved having sex and had a dozen modes. We went down on each other in the hubristically big bathroom of an expensive hotel, so forcefully that we were both raw and laughing before we could finish. She sucked me off in the bathroom of a bad Mexican restaurant. We fucked in my office. I felt her panties bloom into wetness as she drove a rental car through Houston and talked to her mother on the phone. But I had never hit her.

"You didn't want to do that," she said, stretching her arms as the beginning of a deep, sweet yawn.

"I didn't know how to," I said.

"You figured it out."

From then on, hitting became a part of our practice, though it was never a default move. Sometimes she wanted to be held down. Sometimes she wanted me to tie her to the bed. Our moves were unplanned, aside from having to buy restraints. Once we had the fur handcuffs and straps, we came face-to-face with the comedy. ("What is this fur? It's just a piece of carpet.") A t-shirt wrapped around the bedposts became our restraint of choice. Eventually, though, the bits and bobs fell by the wayside. If we brought out the gear, we'd end up laughing at our inability to make knots. Worse, it slowed us down and killed the serendipity of it all. The restraint, the violence, the impact—it had to happen instantly and helplessly during the act. The new fucking had to be brought on by old fucking.

Hitting someone during sex had no inherent value for me. This was not my fantasy. Hitting came up because she wanted it. Then it became freighted with pleasure and anticipation because it worked well, and acutely: for her. The hitting shaded into punishment when she would ask me to abuse her with words as well, to call her a "bad girl" or "a dirty whore." She was in charge of that captioning, and made the choice according to a story I couldn't hear. Despite the intimate nature of hitting a woman while fucking her, you don't necessarily know why that sensation ignites all the other feelings. We never discussed the hitting beyond casual, post-sex locker-room talk: "Was that too hard?" "Am I red?" "Can you bruise if I don't use my knuckles?"

Over time, I stopped thinking about the politics of the act, the satellites of power, subjugation and humiliation. She had chosen an act and told me how she wanted it to happen. As any lover might, she had asked for something. The act was valuable only because it turned her on. If wearing a hat during sex had produced the same rush, I would have done it. Realizing this, I started down a logical chain. What other things could a lover ask for? What would unlock them? Anything could become the cathexis and all rituals could become instrumental to the pleasure. The first buzz was finding a move that unlocked acute, uncontrolled sexual energy. The second, more durable thrill was the prospect of knowing that your partner had a trigger somewhere, a point that would send her down a slide so steep that braking or changing course was not possible. But that lack of control is always twinned with its controlled beginning: only your partner can start the process. Only she can show you where and what to hit. In this setting, your sexual vocabulary expands because of your partner's needs, not your own. You don't need to know the story or unpack the pleasure. Just do as you're told.

Now You Know.

Meaghan O'Connell

We were on our way to a birthday party. This was the first time we'd gone anywhere together that was not someone's bed. He sang the words to a song I didn't know at the top of his lungs, drumming the steering wheel, looking at me, biting his lip. I wanted to laugh, but my eyes just got big.

He turned down the music. "How is work?" he asked.

"Oh, it's all right," I trailed off, not knowing how much to say. I wasn't sure if I'd ever told him what I did for a living, which was babysit and apply to graduate school, while crying.

"Yeah?" he asked. "Any better?" So maybe he did know. I pulled my hair up and leaned back against it on the seat, feeling accomplished. I had met him a few months ago at a bar. We'd had a one-night stand and then many more. He would pick me up at train stops, on street corners, swinging around the block in his ex-girlfriend's station wagon and grabbing me without saying hello when I climbed in. That afternoon I'd seen a video he made of her, that nameless woman, on MySpace. He seemed like he really loved her. I put on more eyeliner in between viewings and resolved not to leave a comment. At the end of the video they were driving those paddleboats in Central Park, the ones that by their very nature make you look even more in love than you already are. I wanted that from him, of course—I wanted the paddleboats and the shared station wagon—the one I used to think I saw all over New York, parked in front of someone else's apartment. I wanted a breakup video like that; I figured I got another chance at it every time I played along with his elaborate, last-minute plans to fuck me.

I looked down at his hand kneading my breasts and back up at him in awe. He exhaled slowly, staring at my face but not at me. He had one hand on the wheel and one hand down my shirt and no eyes on the road. I hid my face and sunk into my seat, pointing at the street out in front of us, laughing and pretending fear. "Drive! Just Drive!" I yelled.

He just smiled and leaned over at a red light and kissed me, wet and haphazard. He took my hand and put it on his hard-on, grinning and quiet as we sped by Prospect Park. I pulled my hands down from over my eyes—I knew the neighborhood—*there was the library*, I thought, pointing through the window to no one, Here are the brownstones, the big sidewalks children have covered with chalk at dusk, waiting for their fathers to come home. I was barreling, tunneling through experience. I was reading ahead in a book that I knew wouldn't end well.

I sat up in my seat again. I cleared my throat in between songs, shifting toward him. "Well, the kid told me yesterday that if I made him go to basketball he would slit my throat."

"What?" he said, laughing like a boy who had just beat a level in a videogame. The rocking back and forth in the driver's seat was subtle, but I was trying to love him so secretly that I saw things in him he didn't mean for me to.

"Ha. Yeah," I went on, getting louder, more confident, "Then he told me he would put my body in a closet, and no one would miss me or care, not even my mother." He said *Oh my god* or something like it while I drew hearts on the window with my fingertip.

David wore a black t-shirt and jeans nearly every time I saw him, but tonight he had on a gingham dress shirt and matching tie. "You look nice tonight," I said, nervous already about what he would say to offend my friends. They had met him when I did, when he tried to take us all to a strip club and fuck more than a few of us at once. They were all terribly worried about me.

He was a painter, a musician, a cinematographer, and a doorman at a fancy hotel. I couldn't believe he did so many wonderful things. He shrugged and said he was a failure at each of them. I was too young to understand that when I met him. All I knew was that when we'd sit up in bed and he'd ask me if a certain painting looked finished, I was always so afraid I'd say the wrong thing. He is from Ithaca but has been here ten years, he would tell me whenever I asked, which was often, because Ithaca meant nothing to me. I usually asked in that moment of fucking him when I would look into his eyes and realize I didn't know his favorite color or middle name, his hometown or him. Afterward, when we'd be getting dressed and my face was red and warm, filled with disbelief for this new thing he was letting me find out about, I'd lean into his shoulder and kiss his neck and hum while he tried to tie his shoelaces. He'd push me away and say things like, "You are good, and I am bad. Find someone good."

"But I want to be bad," I'd say, with newly mustered conviction. These are conversations I leave out in the recounting of our time together to my friends; they are our intimacies, but they sound awful secondhand. He was the third person I had ever slept with. I picked them all up in bars on my nights off.

"How old are you again?" he asked, kneading my left breast with his right hand without looking.

"I'm twenty-three," I told him. *I am*, I thought, *perfectly twenty-three*.

"Yeah so you were about... two years old when this album was made." He laughed and cupped my crotch with his hand. I squirmed and looked out the window for someone different; someone nicer, maybe. "See, I consider everyone the age they were in 1996."

"What?" I asked, under my breath. I was twelve, singing Gloria Estefan on roller skates in the driveway.

"Yeah, see, that's when I was graduating high school, so that's, like, my frame of reference for everyone: 1996."

"Oh," I said, tugging at my cleavage. "I was twelve."

He watched my hands. We both looked down at my dress; I'd bought it that day. It was short and flimsy cotton and turquoise blue, and when I wear it now I safety pin it shut. It looked awful, as dresses that mean everything usually do.

"Yeah so, see, you will always be a sixth grader to me."

I could tell this was a bit he'd rehearsed a few times, so I just looked at him quietly and waited for him to finish.

"The lowest I've gone," he said proudly, "is a first grader."

I swallowed, wishing he would kiss me, but the light had turned green.

•

When we crossed the Brooklyn Bridge and sat down with my friends who laughed with me in the bathroom about what he was wearing, he started leaning in to whisper something dirty in my ear every few minutes. I was beaming, the teacher's pet in my new dress, my hand on his thigh while he breathed warm in my ear. "So," he asked me, "which one of your friends are we going to fuck tonight?" I shrugged, frozen.

He called Marianne over to us after we all sang "Happy Birthday," and she leaned over the table, still dancing while I pouted. She was the prettiest friend of a friend I had, maybe that anyone had. There were blue, bright eyes and a big smile on the kind of woman who figured out early that the only thing more intoxicating than a really beautiful girl was one who acted like a child. She was tan and little and would dance in the middle of the day, on sidewalks, at strangers. It's been years and I still hope she is off somewhere, wishing she were more like me.

He went to buy us drinks and I sat with my bag in my lap, watching him through the crowd. "What're you reading?" she asked. I was sure he was standing somewhere where he could see us, satisfied. I didn't know what else to do, so I took out *Henry and June* and pulled a candle close enough to show it to her. She flipped through, stopping where I'd underlined things about weak men and overzealous women. I knew I could kiss her, could be with her, but that I'd be very angry about it after, when he'd ask me for her phone number. I was just sitting there looking up at her while she fixed my bra strap when he came up from behind and wrapped his arms around her waist. I looked down at my book, opened it, then looked up at him, begging him to remember me, to be kind. They just started dancing, making stupid faces like everyone was watching, which they were. *But it's me*, I said in my head when I looked at him, *Don't you see me?* The girl bounced away to do a few more shots and *She is a better dancer than me*, was all I could think, *I have to leave.*

He grabbed my book from me and shoved it in my bag. I started to cry. I felt like I was having a dream where I needed to breathe but couldn't. He slid in next to me. "You look so hot when you're crying," he whispered. I wanted to hide my face in the neck of every man who would have me. "C'mere," he said, "come back here. Let me suck your tits."

"What?" I said. I cried harder. He kissed me, the tears running in and out of the contours of our faces, saying, *Here. Here is another thing my body can do.* He slipped his hand down the front of my dress and cupped my breast in his hand and kissed me and told me I had to understand, I had to understand he was fucking dozens of other women, and he needed me to know that because he loved me. He had never said any of this out loud before, but we looked at each other in recognition. I traced shapes in the moisture on my glass of beer. I was his friend, he said, and he loved me. He said it and I felt it, but I knew it wasn't enough.

"C'mon," he said, "Don't cry. Do you want me to eat your pussy in the bathroom?" He cocked his head like a puppy, like a concerned father.

"What? No," I said. But he stood up and pulled me by the hand, and I went.

I went and we ran, skipping really, through the crowd, straight into the last bathroom stall, past boys pissing in urinals and girls fixing their hair and their drugs in the mirror.

Ask me what I wanted to be then and I would have said a vessel, a landscape, to disappear. A smart girl a cool girl a girl who makes you forget your mother left you; a girl whose hand you never stop holding when you show her David Lynch movies for the very first time. I wanted to be down for whatever, to wear the right thing and let him take it off, so cool, while he bent me over the desk and fucked me without asking. I wanted to understand him, to save him, to not touch him afterward because I get that he just wants to stare up at the ceiling and laugh for a while after we high-five. I wanted him to take my hand to anywhere. I would have gone wherever.

I still remember how good it all felt, every touch, leggings I don't have anymore around my ankles, stuck in my boots I got at some shitty discount store in Florida. The bathroom was filled with people, but when the music's loud enough, you don't think about it. When your dress is up around your waist with his cock in your mouth, you don't think about other people. It's always thrilling to do things you know better than to do. The voices outside from the people in line yell terrible things that only make you suck harder. You do this instead of crying, you do things you always knew were a bad idea, things you dismissed when you were much younger, but had never tried. You feel brave, being this stupid. In the end, all you are is stupid, but now you know. His cock in your mouth and you're new to sex but finding the way more quickly because now you know for sure.

"You're trying to make me come so I can't fuck anyone else tonight, aren't you?" he said, leaning against the wall, out of breath. "You selfish little girl."

I didn't stop or say a word until he turned me around so that my discount heels and my drunkenness afforded me an angle, my ass just so, turned up and slamming back to meet him, a warm, wet answer to the voices outside the door, yelling, "What the fuck are you doing in there?" I suck in my breath every time he slides in, but my eyes stay on the crack in the door of the bathroom stall. I can see them in line as he moves in and out, and I make little noises through that space just long enough to get the door locked with my free hand and then throw him back up against the wall.

They must have seen us steadying ourselves, pink underwear tangled, somehow, around just one leg. Young voices yelled out that we were disgusting, that we would catch something. We were too far gone. I grabbed the coat hook with my right hand and steadied myself with my left. The rhythm felt essential—I was still in awe of the way our hips seemed to follow dotted lines, sketched out in the air around us, like two subway cars following tracks that were drawn years ago, by fate, under the earth. Any misstep is profound; we feel it together and laugh to ourselves. *Here is what my body can do*, I get to say, for the first time, in my head. Instead of saying things we do things, unraveling with a gesture, because that's what he can give me, and I take it whenever I can.

I put both hands square on the door, like I'm doing a pushup at a 90-degree angle, and fuck him back, hard, just as the opening notes of Simon and Garfunkel's "Cecilia" ring out through the bar. I look back at him to see if he is laughing, too. He leans back against the opposite wall, sweating, shoving his pelvis in and out, tapping my ass in perfect time with the music, smirking. I start to bounce around a little, off of the rhythm, giggling, dancing with him still inside me. He spanks me up-tempo with his right hand and holds my hip up with his left. We laugh, fitting into the space perfectly, like some dirty game of Tetris.

I told him I was about to come, or he asked me, again and again, breathlessly, and I bit my lip and nodded. "C'mere," he says, tenderly. He backs up a few inches to the right, his pants still trapping him around the ankles, and sits down on the toilet. He whispers for me to straddle him, and I stand there shaking, looking down at my feet while he pulls me down over him.

I wrapped my arms around his neck and my pussy around his cock and squeezed my thighs so tightly around his hips; I held him because this was the only time I got to. I fucked him slowly, and deliberately, my tights stretched out across the space between my legs, my pussy on him hard and slow, like it was the last time. Slow, slow, bam. Slow, slow, bam. I balled up his dress shirt in my fists and bit his shoulder and was sad, knowing it would be over soon. He squeezed me to him and bounced me on his lap, and it began to build. I started to sweat behind my knees right when people really started to yell, taunting us about how dirty we were and how terrible it was, my high-heeled boots so blatantly straddling his Converse. I just bit into his collar and shook and came and came and came, screaming silently and then apologizing in his ear, for what I'm not sure. He said nothing, just sat there and picked me up off of him. I stood still, and he stood up and tucked in his shirt and nodded to me silently. I pulled my dress back up from around my waist and he walked out without saying a word.

The door swung open but just enough to make me nervously kick it shut and lock it over terrible words. I pulled my sweaty hair up onto my head and wondered if he was dancing with anyone yet, if he had looked any of those people in the eye on the way out, if I should smile at them, acknowledge that I knew. I wondered if I could just stay here, in this little room until the bar closed, or at least until I caught my breath. I wondered if everyone could smell the sweat and the pussy as much as I did and I looked down at the underwear around my shoe and tucked it into one side of my leggings, where it would stay all night. I listened to people come and go, washing their hands, singing, and waited to summon the bravery it took to walk out. It did not take very long.

Hey, Mr. Tambourine Man

Matthew Gallaway

NOVEMBER, 1997. Driving east on the Long Island Expressway, I listened to the Byrds, whose oscillating harmonies seemed to saturate the low, bleak sky in front of me with the kind of color missing from my own life. I was twenty-nine years old, living with four friends in Park Slope and playing in a band that while perhaps "successful" in an artistic or avocational sense could never—as I had finally admitted a few months earlier—be expected to provide a steady income. Though I possessed a law degree from NYU, I had no stomach for the actual practice and had taken a job selling industrial glass-cleaning solution. I no longer tried to date women but was still deep in the closet in terms of my nonheterosexual "tendencies" (as I tended to think of them). My experience with men was limited to a handful of encounters with older and generally heavier guys who (whether accurately or not) described themselves as "bi" or "bi-curious" in the *Village Voice* personal ads I used to find them; while bisexuality no longer interested me, I hoped that these men would somehow be "less gay" and more forgiving of my inexperience.

The sales job was more interesting than I could have predicted. The work required me to spend a lot of time alone in the car, traveling through ruined postapocalyptic wastelands devoid of vegetation and filled with hulking masses of rusting pipelines, oil drums, and inexplicable machinery. If from the beginning I realized these vistas offered a window into the underbelly of modern civilization—and moreover, that they were a reflection of my deteriorating circumstances—I was beginning to detect a muted beauty in these depopulated, industrial centers, particularly at sunrise or sunset, when the amber tones of light turned the landscape to gold. Recently I had started exploring the online personals in those geographic areas where my sales calls were leading me, or through which I had to pass—i.e., the suburbs—to get there, and answered an ad from a man I will call R (because I have forgotten his name), based in Nassau County, probably in his late thirties and "bi-married."

I drove into the parking lot of the Royal Inn motel in Port Washington/Manhasset, where I spotted his car, an imported make from Germany (this our only means of identification during the pre-photo era of the Internet). I pulled alongside him, fully expecting to drive away after a quick and embarrassed wave, but when he lowered his window and nodded at me in a conspiratorial manner, I liked his somber blue eyes, which if not exactly introspective seemed to possess a degree of kindness and perhaps even resignation I associated with those who have given up more youthful dreams for the comforts and hassles of suburban life. He wore a dark suit.

"Matt?" he asked with a calculated if not unpleasant indifference.

"Hey—R?" I replied, feigning a kind of lassitude belied by the nervous adrenaline I felt cross through my chest and surge to the ends of my fingers, which still gripped the steering wheel.

We sat in silence for a few seconds, negotiating our respective reactions. "So?" he shrugged, which I understood to be a proposal: was I interested enough to take the next step?

"Sure, okay," I nodded. "You?"

"Yeah, sure," he agreed. "We can get a room and talk about it."

I waited in the car while he went to the front desk and paid ($40/two hours). A few minutes later, after a short walk across the parking lot (during which I gave him a $20 bill for my half), we were inside with the horrible floral-print polyester bedspread, faded paint, and brown, threadbare carpet. He sat down on a chair in the corner while I remained a few feet away on the edge of the bed; we continued to coolly observe each other, a display of ambivalence that while obviously an act—as a glance at his crotch or mine would have confirmed—still pleased me, for it made it seem as though we were in control of our desires and not the other way around. We did talk for a few minutes, and it felt good to confide in someone; I told him a little bit about my past and he in turn did the same. He confessed that he had been with men a few times but found the experiences even more trying than I had.

I asked why he continued to look for men, and he just shook his head. "I don't really know," he said, with a kind of remorse I could appreciate. Rather than dwell on it, he looked up at me with a hopeful expression and remarked how cold the room was. "I don't think we paid for heat," he wryly observed. "Do you want to take a shower?"

"That sounds good," I said, as if we were now old friends about to go for a swim in a lake. He disappeared for a moment into the bathroom, where I heard him turn on the shower, and then stepped back into to the room. We both loosened our ties and methodically draped the rest of our clothes (I also had on chinos and a blue dress shirt) over the edge of the chair, where they would not be wrinkled in the fray. I followed him back into the steaming heat of the bathroom and then under the water, where there was no more reason to pretend that our respective desire for the other was anything but shared and fervent. We kissed, tentatively at first and then more forcefully as I grew accustomed to the scratch of his mustache against my beard. He was shorter than me, but stocky and solid (and very hairy), with a build that if once athletic had given way to a middle-aged paunch, which I found more attractive than the type of smooth and "toned" bodies that seemed (and still seem) to define mainstream standards. He also had a seriously big dick—in terms of both length and girth—which though not of primary importance was not irrelevant to my enjoyment as I gripped it in my soapy hands.

We dried off—not really bothering at this point to communicate with anything but glances and hand gestures—and went back to the bed, where we lay under the covers to get warm. During these minutes, which we passed with more kisses and desultory caresses—for he expressed an explicit desire not "to hurry" and I was very content to rub the palms of my hands across his chest and around his nipples—my mind raced with the dissonant implications of having sex with a man I found so attractive combined with a continuing reluctance to believe that it was actually me in this shitty little motel room in Nowheresville, Long Island. I saw myself as though from a distance, in a series of washed-out images that both mocked and alluded to the pornographic overtones of our actions, particularly when—as happened a few minutes later—I put his cock in my mouth and soon after he reciprocated, which despite my obvious enjoyment on one (very elemental) level made it all seem very tawdry and base as I turned my head and saw a golden penumbra seeping around the hideous vertical blinds, and I was struck by the certainty that this was the opposite of any kind of exalted love, the very thing—although I barely recognized this at the time—I craved; but at the same time I could not deny my satisfaction, and eventually I gave myself over to the accreting intensity of the moment, which lasted until it was relieved in the usual manner.

This small but not insignificant feat accomplished for both of us, I looked over at him with a combination of sated desire and a recurrent fear that I would find now find him repulsive, as had always happened to me before. To my relief, I did not, and I even felt a new and different kind of affection as he invited me to lie next to him, where, with his arm cradled around my head, we both dozed off for several minutes before awakening with a jump, after which we hurriedly showered and dressed.

"That was... fun," I said with a calculated nonchalance as we stood at the door and offered him a quick kiss, which he did not refuse.

"Let's do it again," he agreed, as he looked at me through the mirror and straightened his tie.

We met several more times over the next few months, periodically corresponding by email and sharing an almost perfunctory, businesslike demeanor—with very little information exchanged beyond the establishment of a date and a time—and although there was no illusion on either of our parts that the relationship was anything but casual, we developed what I suppose could be classified as a sort of camaraderie if not friendship; when we met, he explained some of his problems at work and with his kids, and I gave him a copy of my band's most recent record. The sex—although largely "innocent" and "safe"—had its awkward episodes, such as the day we decided to try fucking each other, which despite ample amounts of lube remained too painful for either of us to enjoy, or how—whenever he sucked me off—he seemed to gag in a rather tortured and disturbing manner before spitting out the offending fluid and turning to me with his apologetic eyes.

I'm not sure exactly when it ended, although it must have at some point the following spring; there was no break, just a slow fading away. I think of him now with appreciation for providing a kind of warmth that melted away the outer layers of ice in which I had been for so long encased, a necessary step before I could turn to bigger and more important—i.e., more intimate—relationships with men who were as openly gay as I would soon become. While I'm rarely inclined to listen to the Byrds anymore, I remember driving back to Brooklyn, enveloped in their chiming guitars, and how—in the wake of my meeting with R—I was filled with relief and regret, sensing that I had witnessed the end of my youth, along with a torment and fear that had for so long defined it, but which in the ephemeral twilight hovering over New York City seemed to evaporate as the day gave way to the night.

Secondhand News

Tess Lynch

Casey had given a handjob. She was telling us about it in the living room of her parents' house. It had been successful, which was not surprising, considering the fact that the recipient of the handjob was, like us, thirteen years old and could have been brought to orgasm with an oven mitt made of sandpaper; still, the mechanics of handjobs mystified us. To screw up a handjob was to secure a high school experience barren of boyfriends, of love, of hymens exploding like fireworks on prom night or in the backseats of Land Rovers.

"Take off your rings," she instructed. "Don't make the same mistake I made. Why is nobody writing this down?"

I took out a pen and paper. "No rings," I said.

"The next thing you'll need is a lot of Vaseline."

"You keep some in your purse or what?"

"Guys always have it next to their beds." Casey seemed impatient. "So you grab a handful of Vaseline in your ringless hand, and then you make a tight fist around his penis."

"Hold on," said Pam, examining her Smirnoff Ice. "What if we're at my house? Am I supposed to have Vaseline by my bed? Wouldn't that give him kind of a strange idea about me?"

"Don't give him a handjob at your house, then. Give it to him either at his place, or at a concert."

"Beck is at the Troubador in three weeks," I said, but nobody paid any attention. Casey's knuckles were white, her hand a claw around an invisible cylinder. She had paused for effect.

"So Casey," said Pam casually, "on a scale of one to ten, what's your grip like there?"

"Ten being the firmest grip? I'm at about nine."

"Doesn't that hurt him?"

"Stupid," said Casey, repulsed by youth, "that's why I said use Vaseline. The trick here is to imitate a really tight pussy. The thing that gets him off is to think, I can barely fit my thing in here, and his skin stretches over his dick, you know?"

"Pleasure and pain," I contributed.

"Once you're there," urged Pam, "you're gripping it, okay, but what's the movement?"

"Are you just like—" I made a rapid jacking-off motion, "or is it more, you know, like cupping your hand around a waterfall?"

"A waterfall?" Casey dumped the rest of her Smirnoff down her throat. "You guys are so frustrating. I need a smoke break."

We all walked outside and stood by Casey's parents' garage. We took off our shirts and stood in our bras, sharing a clove cigarette.

"God, it feels so good to be out here, smoking, drinking, in a bra," I offered.

"I can't believe I gave Mike a handjob. I feel so weird." Casey hugged herself. Her mother, who was a very religious Mexican woman, parted the curtains in an upstairs bedroom and stared down at us. Casey looked at her and shrugged obnoxiously. I could practically hear her sigh as she flicked off the light and went to bed. "It's like one day I was this naïve child, and then the next day I have some guy's come all over my biology homework."

"He came on your bio?" asked Pam, scandalized. "But you faxed the answers to me!"

"I know. He and I laughed so much about that! 'Oh, will Pam know what that splotch is?' and so on."

"I didn't know," said Pam quietly. "I didn't know it was his jism."

"Casey, explain," I said. "Why did you give him a handjob over your bio homework? Why weren't you guys in a bed or on a sofa or something? Were you at a desk?"

"We were at Century City Mall," Casey revealed enthusiastically.

"This sounds weird," began Pam, "because, like, who brought the Vaseline?"

"He did," said Casey. "Vaseline and a boom box."

We meditated on this as we made our way into the kitchen. Mike suddenly seemed like John Bender sexily superimposed onto Lloyd Dobler. He was the most romantic ninth grader at school. A virile connoisseur of handjobs, he had cared so much for Casey that he had brought both lubricant and melody to their encounter, probably in his backpack.

The Social Experiment

Sarah Dopp

His version:

WE MET SAVING A BABY SEAL on the beach. It almost died! We helped the animal rescue team carry it up the rocky cliff in a big cage, and made sure it was safe. Then we went out for coffee afterward.

♠

Her version:

I posted the ad as a favor to a friend who was researching Craigslist. She wanted to see how frequently W4M Casual Encounters ads got flagged as spammers or prostitutes, so she asked a bunch of friends to post real-enough ads, then track what happened to them. No need to respond to anyone—we just needed to keep her posted on whether or not our ads got deleted.

I kept mine simple.

> *looking for a queer night—w4m—25 (San Francisco)*
> *Me: an androgynous bisexual woman who's not looking for a relationship.*
> *You: an androgynous bisexual man who's not looking for a relationship.*
> *Just a shot in the dark. Are you out there?*

It seemed like the right amount of information. I wanted someone who was just as weird as me, but hotter about it—not someone who thought I was hot because

I was weirder than them. I hoped that putting queer in the subject line would signal sanity to anyone who resented the term bisexual on the grounds that it insisted there are only two genders in the world. And anyone who didn't like weirdos wouldn't respond.

I received...

> *i'm here*

(Yes? And?)

> *hey my name is ryan im 23 new to the bay area email me back if u wana chat.check out my pic*

(Dear Craigslisters, spelling and grammar count.)

> *I am a 39 yr old asian man who is straight and loves woman only. I love getting blowjobs and fucking women regular or anal. I want my salad tossed and cock licked. I dress up nice, make up, long black haired wig, clear 5 inch heels, I have a nice ass for an asian man, I wear balloons for boobs. I'm 5'7" 160 lbs. and muscular medium build. I may consider passable petite fems,TG,TV,TS. But you have to look like a woman, I do not touch or suck cocks. Will masturbate in front of you and you just watch if you want, or participate. Very discreet in my hotel. E-mail me for pic if you want. True photos, NO B.S.*

(Maaaaaybe I didn't think this through.)

> *hi im 19 and would really like to enjoy your company, i have long two tone hair (black and what use to be a red) im sorta new to this. im generally considered to be really attractive, i get asked out alot but im never really looking for a relationship, which makes me sad because i dont like to hurt peoples feelings. im pretty androgynous, and was sorta playing with this strange fantasy in my head where i dress in pretty skirts and blouses and have fun with someone and im way to afraid to*

> *let people know. im sorry if i cant send you a picture but if you decide to respond and we meet up and you dont like the way i look for any way dont worry i never take things personally*

(You're a sweetheart. I'm an asshole. This will never work.)

> *im 29 years old my name haytham im looking for same thing soo letes dowet mail me back pleas thanks good night*

(Sorry, what?)

> Subject: *Foucault would punish me*
>
> *Hi,*
> *For saying that I look androgynous. I don't. Too many muscles, too much hair on my face, not enough on my head.*
> *But I think that way.*
> *So, unless your heart's desires were already fulfilled, I'm out here.*
> *Male. Bisexual.*
> *Not looking for a relationship.*

(Foucault? WHO THE FUCK RESPONDS TO A PERSONALS AD LEADING WITH A REFERENCE TO FOUCAULT?)

I wrote back.

Two emails, an analysis of facial hair, and a casual reference to BDSM later, I agreed to a latté at 5. He then sent a photo: an unposed shot of five people standing in a hallway, bored. He was the bald one with his hands jammed into his torn jacket pockets and eyes half closed, looking stoned. He looked to be about forty-five, but he was also far away, and in a distinctly unattractive pose. He could just as easily have been thirty. Or sixty.

I mumbled, "Fuck it," and sent him a recent photo of me looking adorable. Shiny glasses and a shaved head, cuddled up in a hoodie with a huge grin, looking as "twenty-five years old" as you can get. I made sure to mention that I had plans later that night, so this was just coffee.

I was ready for a war—ready to be defiant, precocious, independent, unavailable, or even pathetically self-absorbed if it came to that. I could work it.

I wore jeans and a t-shirt with no makeup, knowing it made me look like a boy. Cleavage and eyeliner on me are hot, but boy mode is a little bit awkward and homely when it plays out on my body, despite being important to me. My first line of defense was in place.

He was already at the counter of Café du Soleil, hunched over a hardcover library book when I walked in. My initial impressions were off. He was older—fifty, fifty-five. It showed around his eyes—some combination of too much brow-furrowing and too much laughing—but he looked gentle.

He bought me a latté. Actually, two. We talked longer than I expected.

He had a thing for dead philosophers, so I challenged him to explain their primary theories to me in clear terms. It was a test, really, but then again everything on a first date is a test. And I sure as shit wasn't going to sleep with the guy, so I was just having fun at that point. Learning something. Getting my latté's worth.

When Foucault came up again, I asked about the "punishment" he referred to, and got him talking about "whips and stuff." He paused and added, "But I don't do that. Definitely not for me. So if that's what you're looking for..." He trailed off, laughing.

Two strikes in one sentence. Strike one: He thinks I'm here because I'm looking for something. Presumptuous. Strike two: As a matter of fact, I do like getting the shit paddled out of me by a loving, skilled hand, and if he thinks that's a joke, then fuck him.

I settled back into my chair, feeling victorious. I had beaten him, and he didn't even know it yet. Moving on.

After the second latté was long gone, he prompted, "So you probably have to get going."

I wanted to say no, actually I don't. Actually, you can tell me about Foucault all night. Just as long as I don't have to touch you, you can keep me company forever. But it came out like, "Yeah, I should get going."

We gathered our things and he started to walk me uphill. "My car's right here," I said, pointing a few feet away.

"Then I'll take you this way," he said as he kept walking up the side street.

I took a quick inventory of my bag. I had at least two pens and a set of keys I could stab him with. And my cell phone. I followed.

A third of the way around the block-wide circle he was walking us in, I told him the truth: the ad was a research favor to a friend. A social experiment. Not for me.

"So you're not actually interested in anything," he said.

I picked my words carefully. "I didn't plan on responding to anybody."

"If you're not interested in anything, you can just say, 'Thank you, I'm not interested.'"

My eyes widened. He was offering me a clear script for rejection. I was always so bad at giving those, and he made it sound easy. I liked him for it.

"Okay," I said, acknowledging his point, but not saying any more.

With sunglasses on, he looked forty. When we turned the last corner, I gave him a hug and said, "Thank you." He thanked me back, and we each nodded as I walked to my car. I knew I'd never see him again. That was nice.

I was going to drive home. I meant to drive home. Instead, I drove to the bookstore and found *Foucault for Beginners*, bought it, sat down in a café chair, and read the first half of it. Then I drove to the ocean.

I sat there in my car in the dark with my windows cracked just enough to hear the waves but not so much that I could get mugged and raped. I knew that when I went home, I would curl up and hate myself. I would hate that my grandmother was dying, hate that it had been three years since my last partner left, and hate that I hadn't trusted anyone since then. I knew it would be another night of me rolling my entire body up in a blanket as tightly as I could, like a burrito, just to feel held when I was alone.

I pulled out my fancy cell phone and checked the anonymous email account I used for Craigslist. It already had a message from him.

> *Sarah,*
> *Let me know if your friend designs another social experiment that would involve me being in your arms again. Or you being in my arms again.*
> *I would even happily do it without the scientific method being involved.*
> *Give me a day or two or three to find your Foucault Made Simple.*
> *And, if I were somehow to be mentioned in a blog, I would prefer my name be randomized.*
> *Not that I read any of those things.*

I wrote back.

He was at my apartment within an hour.

In the time it took for him to come over, I got myself ready. Loose pajamas, lots of deep breathing, some prep work on my distracted clit with a vibrator, and two condoms placed carefully by the lamp. In exchange for the company, for not having to be alone, I was committed to a course of action: I would put out, I would put out well, and I would do so against my gut reactions, violating my own comfort zones, and ensuring I'd never ever want to see him again, which was fine. He'd already made me relax enough that this needed to be stopped.

I forgot my doorbell was broken, and it took a while to hear his knocking. When I finally answered the door, he was shaken—nervous he'd gotten the wrong house maybe, or that I'd changed my mind.

I laid down on the bed. He pulled up a chair.

After some talking, he said to me, "Would you like me to just wrap my arms around you for a while?"

"Yes, please," I said, and shifted to make space for him.

He lay down next to me, his coat and shoes still on, and spooned me from behind in a full hug. Then he stayed there. I stayed there. With more relief than I can articulate, I lay there in his arms like that for literally over an hour. Not moving, not talking, just breathing together. Somehow he knew that that was all I needed, and I can't tell you what it meant to me that that was all he did, that he just held me. I sunk into him with so much relief that I cried a little, but I kept my body as still as possible so he wouldn't notice. My cunt unclenched and stopped fearing what I'd do to it. And I breathed, and rested, and sighed and held onto his arms, and stopped hating everything in myself and everyone in the entire world for more than an hour.

Eventually, I rolled over—very slowly—to thank him face-to-face. I meant to nuzzle my forehead into his neck, but instead I kissed him through his moustache and beard. I felt his embrace change and something unlocked in both of us. The thank-you turned into a demand, and within seconds his hands were on my breasts and he was kissing his way down my belly to my legs.

I have no idea what was fast or slow—I was still too high from being held. But I do know his scratchy face was already between my legs before I had time to consider the usual pros and cons of dissociating.

His tongue seemed quick (or maybe I was already soaked—just as likely) because the next thing I realized, his lips were rolling around like I was his own personal Slip 'n Slide. He was breathing me in and dancing around my hairy skin like this was all for him. Like I was some kind of fancy wine tasting, paired with the best meat a foodie could ask for.

And then he focused, found my clit, and started testing out rhythms and angles. My breathing was his feedback.

I never come from oral sex. I'm too sensitized to the manic jackhammer that is my Hitachi. Too apologetic about how long my poor partners' heads have to stay down there suffocating, their tongues exhausted and demoralized by the fruitless effort. Too concerned that pushing for momentary satisfaction might fuck up something important, or worse, make me dependent on something I can't control. When I finally accepted all this years ago, I stopped avoiding oral sex and started enjoying it for what it was—an appetizer. Or sometimes a subtle dessert.

I knew how it would go. He would lap at my clit for a while, slip his tongue in and out of my cunt for good measure, do several rounds of everything with a really determined look on his face, and then start to slow down. At that point, I'd change my panting to a series of slow, content sighs and then touch his chin gently, inviting him back up to kiss me. Faking orgasms is unethical, but I have no problem faking satisfied.

He played it out differently. Once he found some good angles on my clit, he pushed two fingers into my cunt without warning. They went in easily and he angled them straight for my G-spot, and started rubbing. I switched to moans.

Gently, he increased the intensity on both my clit and my G-spot as he played with them. It felt like they were connected to each other by piano strings, and every tap and lick strummed away at me until my hand pressed down on the back of his head. When my responses wouldn't go any louder, he slowed down. I squirmed, moaned, and whimpered, "thank you," ready to welcome him back up. It wasn't an orgasm, but it was plenty satisfying, and I'd have no problem fucking him now.

He took his fingers out, but stayed down there for a bit—breathing me in, exploring me, enjoying it. I let my body relax and my mind wander to how I should get his pants off for a blowjob. And whether I should try to get him off that way or just tease him a little. I couldn't tell yet if he was the type to come once or twice.

I snapped back to the moment when he started going again—licking my clit like I was a melting popsicle, and putting his fingers back inside me. The same scene repeated, and he brought me up to a higher peak. I was shocked, moaning, and babbling stupidly, "Oh my god, you're still going, oh my god..." Embarrassed by my own confusion and noise, I pushed the pillow over my face and bit it. My body rocked and bucked, and I'm grateful I didn't knock his face too hard as he found my limit again, and then relaxed.

I threw the pillow off, gasped, tried to talk, couldn't. He was still down there. I touched his head, got him to make eye contact with me, and got him to see the look on my face. He found my hand and held it.

Then he went after me again.

This time there was no sense to be made, no way to describe what was going on, no words to thank him, no way to express how my body felt, except to scream and thrash and whimper and clutch his hand so hard I thought his fingers might break. Waves of something that I barely recognized as "a different kind of orgasm" pulsed through me and I lost all feeling in my feet. I tried not to hurt him. I was gone.

At some point—I don't know when—he crawled back up to hold me. I was shaking. I couldn't speak. We rested.

I kissed him, and both his beard and moustache were soaked in me. He tried to keep kissing me, but it felt like trying to breathe through a wet washcloth, so I propped myself up my elbow to look at him. He was still wearing his coat and shoes. I smiled.

We started to undress each other.

As soon as he was naked, the situation became real to me, and I remembered how uncomfortable I was with it. Averting my eyes, I excused myself to the bathroom.

I had to pee.

When I came back into the room, he was sitting on the edge of my bed, bare and humble. The whole picture of him—his face, his skin, his legs—made me stop ten feet away. I was dizzy. In the low light, he looked seventy.

The expression on his face stunned me. He was open, hopeful, a little sad, and waiting. He was a man, a human being, sitting there on the edge of a bed, liking a girl. All of his armor was down and for a minute, he looked angelic.

I tried to remember what was next. I would suck his cock. That was next. I would slide my tongue up and down it, tease him, and take it all into my mouth. I would lie him down and invite him to relax by varying the speed of my sucking, showing him I was in control, letting him know I had it. And then... and then I hoped I'd figure out what came next after that.

I wasn't really sure I wanted to see it. It could be wrinkly. Or dirty. Or deformed. Or maybe he wouldn't be able to get it up. I would deal.

I stepped forward, and let it come into view. His cock. His cock was hard and pointed upward toward his chin. And I swear to god, it was the size of a Mission burrito.

I stared at it. I looked up at his eyes where he still held that hopeful, waiting expression, and then I looked back at his cock. There was no way I was gonna try to fit that thing into my mouth, and I had no other plan.

Mercifully, he reached out and invited me in for a hug. The hug turned into a kiss, and the kiss turned into him laying me down on my back again. Then he kissed my breasts, my belly, and my cunt, and before I could say anything, his fingers and tongue took control again, and he carried me up to another orgasm. I had no idea this was possible.

He slid back up my body, kissed me, and studied my face for a while. I was trying to convey total shock, but I really don't know what he saw. He started to slide back down my body, asking, "Do you want more of my tongue?"

"NO!" I cried out, my volume surprising me.

He stopped, pulled his hands off me, and started to back away with his palms raised, like someone who'd been caught by the police. I'd given a signal that consent had ended, and he was trained to remove himself first and ask questions later.

I caught him by the shoulder before he could get too far, and changed my shaking head to a nod. "No," I repeated. "I want you to fuck me."

His face changed, and he straightened up. "Oh. I can fuck you," he said, almost professionally. "Do you have a rubber? A condom?"

I breathed, nodded, and pointed to the lamp. He picked one up, opened it, and slid it on. Then he climbed on top of me missionary style, and pushed himself inside me.

With his face in the pillow, I could stare past him, over his shoulder to the ceiling, and finally—for the first time all goddamned night—finally dissociate from the experience. He was big, and he filled me, so it was easy to moan along with his motions. But after all those orgasms, knowing the focus had finally shifted to him was a relief. He was rhythmic, methodical, and he came with a loud groan that made me want to hug him. So I did.

After we held each other for a while and caught our breaths, I thanked him for being wonderful to me.

His response surprised me. "Why would anyone not be wonderful to you?"

"I don't give most people the chance," I said.

"I'm glad you let me sneak up on you, then."

"Me, too."

He started to ask questions. Questions like, was I seeing anybody and how often did I do this? Questions gently leading toward, "Is there room in your life for me?"

I told him I've been single for three years, and I have a one-night stand about once a month. It's maintenance, I guess. And it's enough for me. I need my autonomy way too much to be in any relationship.

"It's possible to be in a relationship and not give up your autonomy," he told me. I looked at him blankly, not knowing how to process this paradox.

He read my confusion and tried to explain. "We're queers," he said. "We get to make our own rules."

Oh, you're good.

We talked for a while about what the rest of our lives are like. Then he interrupted one of his own sentences, saying, "I didn't kiss you enough." He kissed me. "I didn't fuck you enough."

"I thought you fucked me very well," I said, still a little dizzy.

"That's not what I meant," he said as he sat up on his knees and scooched back on the bed. I stared in disbelief as he opened the other condom and rolled it onto his now hard again dick. I wasn't sure how much more of this I could take.

With more power than I anticipated, he rolled me over onto my stomach, grabbed me by the hips, and pulled me up onto my hands and knees. I almost said, "yes sir" out loud, but I bit it back.

Upright on his own knees behind me, he pushed his cock into my cunt again, hard. A surge of pain filled my abdomen as the burrito hit my cervix, but it melted into laughter and tingling just as quickly as it arrived. I rocked against him, delirious, wondering what the hell this man eats, wondering how I was going to explain this to my friends, wondering what kind of movie I'd fallen into. He slid his cock as far out as he could without leaving me, and pulsed gently with just the head inside me, waiting, until I whimpered and wiggled to his satisfaction.

Then he slammed into me, and I screamed. He repeated: out, pulse, slam. Out, pulse, slam. Then just the slamming—slam, slam, slam—until my arms gave out and my head was on the mattress and I was screaming into the pillow and, fuck, coming again. He kept going, past the point where he'd lost me, where I was off floating, lying on the ceiling and looking down at him shaking my limp body on his dick like a rag doll who'd been bad, until he came again, hard and loud with a noise that sounded almost like a roar.

And then he collapsed on top of me.

He didn't spend the night.

The next day, he sent me an email that read:

> *Perhaps we could get a latté sometime.*

•

His version:
We met at a coffee shop. I don't really remember how, but we just started talking.

The Feeling

Peter Raffel

My first kiss was nothing like a movie. There was no spectacle or majesty to it; no real emotion behind the thing to justify it. It was sweet but also scary, like the butterflies in my stomach had somehow exploded out of my mouth in some bizarre form of throwup. I wasn't confident or suave or anything like that; I was quiet and scared and pale and my leg kept on shaking. It was 1 a.m. on New Years Day of 2008 and I was on a boat in the middle of the Caribbean. Her name was Lindsay and was from Georgia and was the first girl ever to whisper in my ear, "Wanna hook up?"

I said yes.

I grew up, like all kids do, with a fascination with kissing before I really even knew what it was. I never went as far as practicing on a mirror or a stuffed animal, but I kept it in the back of my mind always, like a faraway goal. That is, until I turned fourteen and realized that, despite what I told my friends, I was a mouth virgin and I was growing old.

The boat was massive, but most important to my cousins and myself was the Teen Disco, which we'd read about on the website as a place for teens to dance and hang out. We'd joked about it; said that we were going to go and "get crazy." However, something deep inside us told us it was more than that: it was a place where we could live out our fantasies, a place full of possibility, a place of God knows what. We realized on the first night there that what it was, actually, was a small room with a bit of a dance floor, a place to get soda, Guitar Hero, and a Foosball table. It was bright and strange. I stood there in my tight Hollister polo and jeans, with braces on my teeth and long hair sweeping across my brow, I was very upset. Let's just say it was a drastic change from the Freshmen Luau earlier that year, where I'd danced with thirty-nine girls in one night. As far as I could see, there were only a few girls at the foosball table and a kid with a unibrow playing Guitar Hero. One of these girls was Lindsay.

When we first met, I hadn't thought much of her. She had big eyes and freckles that danced across her face, a smile that seemed to simply to know me, even before I'd said anything. Awkwardly, I'd introduced myself: "Hi, I'm Peter, what's your name?" We talked for a brief five minutes before my cousins and I left to go explore the rest of the boat and I remember thinking that I had accomplished something there; talking to a girl in front of my two older relatives, with no shame or nervousness.

A day later we were at the Teen Disco, her and I, grinding awkwardly there as she rubbed against me. The bulky camera in my pocket clumsily pressed up against her. And it was there, minutes after midnight, that she whispered in my ear, "Wanna hook up?"

She took my hand and led me out of the disco, and I felt my body go numb and my throat dry out and close up, my palms sweat feverishly. She led me out onto the deck, then stopped.

"Okay, here is good," she said. And then she kissed me.

It was teethy, and it tasted bad; it felt awkward, like we were both trying to win in a thumb war with our tongues. There was a moment where I attempted to raise her up onto the railing of the boat, trying to lift her and place her up there while still kissing her, but either I couldn't lift her, or she didn't want to, or a combination of both, so I just let it go. We kissed for three minutes and then stopped.

She paused for a second. "You're a good kisser," she said.

"Thank you," I said, pausing, and then adding, "So are you."

But you aren't really, I thought. Either that, or this was the way making out was going to be for forever.

A drunk man danced near us, his t-shirt wet and his beer belly exposed as he swayed around the pool. After we stopped and had exchanged a few words, she headed off to bed, and I sat on a deck chair with my head in my hands until I finally stopped shaking and was able to get up.

We hooked up again the next night in the back of the boat and this time I succeeded in putting her up onto the railing, as she guided my hand underneath her shirt and onto her breast. We went at it for about fifteen minutes before she pulled away, smiling at me. I tried to kiss her neck a bit, like I'd seen in movies, but she seemed bored and uninterested and so I stopped after a couple seconds.

Two nights later we hooked up in the handicapped restroom on the bottom floor of the boat, where I'd felt up her bare ass awkwardly and she'd dry humped me while I sat on the toilet. She asked me how far I'd gotten with a girl, and I said second base, lying flat-out. She said she'd been to third base and then went back to dry humping me.

When I finally found out, through several days of detective work, that she was hooking up with someone else on the boat, she denied it. She told me, as her and Brock stood in front of me at the Teen Disco, that he was just her cousin. I spent a good minute looking over the pair, trying to find similar features that they shared. There were none. I stormed out of the room as she chased after me, trying to deny what she'd done. I pointed out his number, which was etched on her arm with Brock written above it. That was when she finally gave up.

I was absolutely furious as she sat down, trying to explain herself to me. "I just broke up with my boyfriend, and I wanted to go back and brag to him about how many guys I'd hooked up with."

"I just can't believe you cheated on me," I said back, anger rising in me. But even then, as I contemplated this statement, I realized she hadn't cheated. For someone to cheat, you had to be going out with someone; you had to go on dates. We'd done none of that. We'd hooked up three times on a cruise ship. I'd worn the same jeans every time. I'd worn socks with sandals one of the times. We weren't dating.

"You're funny, you're cute, you're a great kisser," she said, stumbling out words.

"I know," I said back, knowing that I sounded like an asshole, but not really caring. "Why did Brock agree to this? He must have known that you were with me; what the fuck is his problem?"

"He's Polish," she answered. I was fuming. I had been played; I'd been used for sexual favors, for a story she could tell people when she got back about how she'd gotten with a cute Chicago boy, and he'd put her up on a railing.

I tried to yell at her, tried to tell her that she'd hurt me, but the words came out with no real meaning, sounding pointless, and eventually I just got up, went back into the Teen Disco, and grinded with some Spanish girls before going to bed.

The fury only lasted until I got off the plane, though, because when I did I started talking. I told the swim team about my wild cruise, about how I'd hooked up with a girl three times, then caught her in a lie and totally "owned her." I told them about how I had Lindsay take a picture of me and Brock before storming out of the Disco; I told them about how I'd felt her up two times. I told friends and anyone who would listen. I talked for about six months before I finally stopped and moved on.

At the time, it seemed as if she'd betrayed me intentionally, as if she'd set out to do me harm and break my heart. But after a while I realized there wasn't any emotion to it at all, it was simply making out at one in the morning on a cruise ship. It was simply me sitting with my head in my hands on a deck chair before I finally was able to pick myself up and head back to my room.

Back at the room I stared at myself in the mirror, weighing the night heavily while my father and sister were in the other room. It was a mistake. I was here with my family, who I had grown up with. I assumed that was what making out was. Everyone has a family they go home to after they make out.

A Walking Culinary Cemetery

Maria Diaz

WHEN MY FRIEND TURNED THIRTY, she met it with her usual positive attitude, incredible sense of humor, and lots of Jäger bombs (don't judge until it's 1:30 a.m. and you get offered one, okay?). It was me, at twenty-six, who lost it. Here is how it started.

Her party was going to happen at a new restaurant, and due to San Francisco's draconian alcohol licensing policies, the restaurant had no booze available for purchase on the night of her birthday. So, instead, we had to bring our own. Fifty guests, each wielding about three bottles of alcohol. I was determined to drink it all.

By the end, with everyone drunkenly saying good-bye, and about to split a cab with a friend back home, I decided, as so many obnoxious drunk bitches before me, that the night was not done yet. I asked a friend to wait while I went inside and found something/someone else to do while everyone went home, and with those famous last words, found someone. What did he look like? Older, taller, and most importantly, alive and wanting to actually do something. By "something," I mean have sex as soon as possible. I had never laid eyes on this person before, and all of a sudden, it was imperative that we do it.

As my friends went away, no doubt talking about me via their goddamn iPhones, I made out with him while we waited for a cab. Once in it, he grabbed me and whispered in my ear, "I really want to fuck you." I rolled my eyes. Why do all drunk dudes say the same thing?

The rest of the night was fairly boring. All I could remember was that he would open his eyes wide and shake his head in a circle while he was trying to make me come, and I had to turn away to stop myself from laughing. Eventually, we fell asleep.

The following morning, I braced myself for the typical sobering post-hook-up awkwardness, that same conversation I've had so many times before: where you list all the things you're doing so you can avoid spending more time there, talking about how fun it is.

And then he says to me: "I wonder if anyone saw me leave with you. That wouldn't be very good for my reputation, after the whole vegansexual thing."

"Vegansexual?" I ask.

"Yeah," he says. "I just wrote about vegansexuality for my column."

I laughed. He was being 100 percent serious. (For those of you who aren't familiar, a "vegansexual" is a vegan who only has sex with other vegans. I am not vegan.)

He was so serious that a while later, over cups of green tea, brewed for just the right amount of time, he showed me the article.

Here is a little snippet:

> *"Nonvegetarian bodies," said one female subject, "(are) literally sustained through carcasses—the murdered flesh of others." If you really are what you eat, then the body of a meat eater is, as one vegan commentator put it, "kind of a graveyard for animals." You don't need to be a certified sexpert to appreciate that some vegans would be turned off by the thought of exchanging bodily secretions (like sweat, spit, scents, and... well, you get the picture) with such walking culinary cemeteries."*

I've always thought of myself as an adorable beacon of adorableness wrapped in a black hoodie and smelling faintly of dark chocolate, espresso, and sunflowers (or bourbon, but it depends on the time of day) but I guess "walking culinary cemetery" works, too. The fact that he went so far as to show me the piece was off-putting. Why did he even invite me back here? From the minute we met, after I had walked over to where he was across the room, as everyone was getting ready to leave, the very first words I slurred at him were: "Dude, I'm so not vegan!"

The kicker, however, really was at the end:

> *"Yet I persist in hoping because the heart wants what it wants, and I know, in my heart, that I want to be with someone with whom I can enjoy the ineffably unique bond that only exists in the coupled soul of two deeply bonded vegan lovers."*

Except for, you know, that unique bond that is shared between two hammered people at a party who talk to each other for ten minutes and then decide to go home together. I mean, I get it. A drunk ho is a drunk ho whether or not she stuffs her face with goat cheese and fried chicken or Teese and Boca Burgers, but if a dude can rise above eating steaks, can't he rise above the call of easy sex? I guess he can say that while his brain is vegan, his dick was merely vegan-flexible.

Never Have I Ever

Tyler Coates

I DIDN'T HAVE MANY FRIENDS AROUND when I returned home for the summer after my freshman year of college, so I had fully intended to spend my days working at the local state park and my evenings locked in my room getting drunk on Zima, watching Internet porn, and chatting with other gay dudes over my parents' incredibly slow dial-up connection. I was certain by the end of my second week at home that I would probably not get much out of my summer break, and I longed for those humid months to fly by as quickly as possible so that I could return to school and have actually friends to hang out with while shirking my homework for frantic, late-night masturbation.

I wasn't out yet, nor did I have a complete understanding of my sexuality. Sure, I knew I liked guys, but I also thought I liked girls. I spent most of my high school years developing intense, obsessive crushes on my female classmates, but they were (conveniently, I suppose) out of my league. I was a late bloomer and "sensitive." I was lanky, standing at five feet and eleven inches and weighing in at about one hundred and twenty-five pounds. I still parted my hair in the middle about a year after every other guy my age went for a basic crew cut, and it perfectly framed my freckled cheeks, still puffy with baby fat. My legs and arms were emaciated, and my midsection was slightly round from a diet comprised of pizza and premium malt beverages. I didn't have an exercise regime beyond walking to and from the car. Naturally, I didn't possess the confidence to fully pursue the girls I liked, and I was generally afraid of the boys I knew (they were all straight anyway).

I got a random IM one night from a guy named Patrick who had graduated with me the year before. "my brother and me are going to have people over tomorrow night," he typed in a yellow font on a navy-blue background. "prolly just to drink some beers and play cards or something. you can come by if you want." I weighed my options: I could hang out with my parents until they went to bed, knowing it was safe to start trolling the chat rooms for nearly silent phone sex, or I could kill a few hours drinking real beer with real people. It was a Friday night, and since I worked the next morning at ten I figured I'd spend a few hours at Patrick's and head home before it became too late.

I arrived at Patrick's house at around nine thirty on Friday night, and I was immediately surprised that there were only four cars in the driveway. Patrick greeted me at the door with a nonchalant hello, to which I returned with an equally disaffected wave and a "Hey..." I followed him down the hall to the back of the house. Ben was waiting in the enclosed sunroom, watching TV and drinking from a plastic tumbler. He nodded at me as Patrick showed me to a table on which sat two-liters of soda and bottom-shelf alcohol.

"So," I began as I raced to mix a rum and Coke, "who else is supposed to come tonight?"

"You were the only person who said they'd definitely come," Patrick said. "I called Brian Clark and TJ Moore, but they were going to some movie in Fredericksburg with a few girls."

"My friend Kelly said she might stop by later," Ben said, not looking up from the TV.

I slurped my drink quickly and it was about half-empty when Ben suggested playing some sort of game. "There's nothing on TV anyway," he said as he lit a cigarette—inside the house!—and passed the pack to Patrick. I turned down a smoke; it was a few years before I finally relented and realized, as most twenty-year-olds do, that smoking does make you look pretty fucking cool. Ben divided the cards between the three of us and we started to play Asshole, which was the default drinking game when you were too bored and unoriginal to come up with something interesting to do while you drank.

By the time we had finished two rounds of Asshole, I was both the titular character of the game and quite tipsy. I wasn't a big drinker; by that time I had probably only really been drunk twice, and it certainly didn't take much to put me under. The brothers got bored with Asshole, luckily, and decided to switch to Never Have I Ever. Considering I had pretty much not done anything, I figured I could relax for a few rounds and sober up while Patrick and Ben got drunk.

"Never have I ever smoked weed." Ben and Patrick took a sip of their drinks.

"Never have I ever thrown up in a public place." Ben and Patrick drank, again.

"Never have I ever jerked off at work." Again, they took sips.

I started to get bored, and took drinks when one of the other guys did. "What! When have you taken a piss while driving?" they asked. "Well, I haven't," I replied. "But I am thirsty."

"Never have I ever been to a strip club." Patrick took a drink.

"Never have I ever seen Dad naked." Ben took a drink.

"Never have I ever stolen porn from 7–11." Patrick took a drink.

"Never have I ever dated a guy named Thad." Ben took a drink.

"Wait, what?"

Patrick and Ben both turned to me, then back to each other. They started laughing, nearly falling out of their chairs. "I, uh, dated a guy named Thad," Ben said. "I'm a big homo, you didn't know?"

I was confused. He said it with such carelessness while Patrick laughed. Patrick, who I had heard, along with the rest of the guys on the soccer team in high school, use the word "faggot" so liberally when we were in school. And Ben was gay! His brother, the faggot! I tried to mask my astonishment by continuing the game.

"Uh—never have I ever failed a class?"

We kept drinking. We finished the rum and I moved onto the vodka. We gave up on the game. Patrick and Ben chain-smoked as I sat there watching them, slowing becoming more and more light-headed.

"Don't worry, we have a futon," Ben said as he took a long drag.

I managed to push myself out of my chair and stumbled into the bathroom. I laid on the floor and slumped over the toilet, the cool porcelain balancing out the sweat on my face. I dozed off a bit until I felt a tap on my shoulder, then a light shaking.

"Hey." It was Ben. "You should get in bed."

I groaned. "Okay." He helped me off the floor and led me to a dark bedroom. I collapsed on the bed. Ben walked over to his desk and opened a WinAmp playlist and began to shuffle through his music. He started playing Ryan Adams's Heartbreaker and laid down on the bed next to me, leaving ample room between us.

"Are you feeling all right?" he asked.

"I guess so," I said, turning over—not to face him, really; just to project myself in his direction. "I don't know if I've ever had that much to drink so quickly."

"Well, you've got to start sometime."

"I guess so."

I realized that during our brief exchange we had moved closer to each other. We weren't touching, but I was close enough that I could feel the warmth of his body through my clothes.

Then he turned to me and started kissing me on the cheek, which was sobering enough that I found the energy to immediately turn over so that I could kiss him back.

I'd never made out with anyone before, and I had no idea what to expect after years of desperately wanting someone to kiss. I was surprised at how the stubble around his lips felt on mine, how hot and wet his tongue felt sliding in my mouth. Despite not knowing exactly what to do, it felt natural, as if I was instinctively certain that this is what I was made to do. He rolled on top of me, pressing his body onto mine as I ran my fingers through his hair and then down his back.

And before I knew it, he was going down on me.

He was quick, moving from my mouth down to my pants in just a few seconds. He quickly pulled them off and put me in his mouth. I was almost too shocked from making out with a guy that I wasn't quite sure how to process the idea that my cock was suddenly in his mouth. At the time, however, I wasn't analyzing it too much, but was rather enjoying my first blowjob without focusing on the fact that I was receiving it just ten minutes after my first kiss.

After a few minutes of what was, as far as I knew, the best oral sex ever, Ben came back up and started to make out with me again, casually rolling us over so that I was laying on top of him. Well, it was about as casual as you can be when you're silently trying to tell the guy whose dick you just sucked that it's now his turn. I have never been one for picking up subtle social cues, but I got it. I figured I should make my move before Ben started making more obvious hints, such as pushing down on my head or face-fucking me.

I tried to be smooth, removing his shirt first and kissing his chest as I made my way down to his waist. That is what you are supposed to do, right? Rather than just go right at it? Obviously, my only experiences with blowjobs were watching them being performed in a QuickTime movie, and things happened pretty quickly in those circumstances. I mean, they only had about fifteen minutes to get shit done!

I finally decided to stop stalling and began pulling off Ben's pants, slowly reaching my hand down the front of his boxers. I sort of gasped when I wrapped my hand around his cock; I hadn't seen it yet but could tell that it was massive: not just long, but pretty thick as well. It's fairly disheartening to compare the size of your own penis to the first one you see in real life, especially when you suffer from penis dysmorphia.

So then I blew him! I can't imagine, really, how to put it any way other than that: I sucked Ben's dick. I had no idea what I was doing, and feeling him harden in my mouth was something I wasn't expecting as it took some effort to get his cock in my mouth in the first place. I pushed my mouth down and back up again a few times, simultaneously hoping that I was doing a good job and that it wouldn't be long until I could quit and Ben could return to sucking me. He started to guide me along with his hand on the back of my neck, giving me slight encouragement (twice gasping, "Teeth!"). As I kept going, however, his grip on my neck began to loosen, and he started running his hand through my hair as I intermittently slurped on his cock and stroked it with my hand. Although I wasn't totally sold on sucking his dick, hearing Ben moan encouraged me to keep going.

We fooled around for about an hour, rolling around on the bed, alternating whose cock was in whose mouth, until it was clear that the vodka Ben was drinking was keeping him from finishing. He moved me on top of him and instructed me to finish, so I sat there, straddling his stomach, trying not to feel self-conscious about someone watching me jerk off. I managed to come (which, honestly, was not difficult), and, as he rolled over to find the t-shirt he was wearing earlier to wipe himself off, I moved to the other side of the bed. My first reaction was not to crawl under the covers next to Ben and fall asleep, but to get dressed.

"What are you doing?" he asked.

"Just putting my pants back on," I said, trying to cover up any indication that I wasn't yet prepared to analyze what had just happened, much less lie naked in bed with the boy with whom I had just "done stuff."

"Are you okay?" he asked. "Are you getting weird about this?"

"No, I'm fine," I replied, crawling under the covers fully clothed. I laid there with my back to him and closed my eyes, feeling both nervous and strangely comfortable with Ben's body pressed against mine, his left arm wrapped around my waist.

I woke up the next morning with a headache and the confusion one experiences upon waking up unexpectedly in someone else's bed. I must have shaken with surprise when I got up, because Ben was also awake. He gave me a sleepy smile and slid over toward me, putting his arms around me again. He started to kiss me, and any awkwardness I felt before falling asleep and again when I woke up seemed to disappear immediately once I had my arms wrapped around him. I was still fully clothed, but I could feel him through his boxers pressing against me. I slid my hand down his back, sliding it below the elastic waist and to his front. I grabbed his cock, and he was on top of me, sitting upright with his legs straddled around my chest. He slowly moved closer and closer to me, and I pulled down his underwear and held his cock, stroking it as I looked up at him. He didn't say anything, but continued to push himself toward my mouth.

About five minutes later I heard a feminine cough from the other room, which was shocking enough to incite me to nearly spit Ben's dick out of my mouth, as if someone had just performed the Heimlich maneuver on me in order to keep me from choking on a penis lodged in my throat. I suddenly realized that we were, in fact, in Ben's parents' home, and there I was sucking him off while his mother walked around the house. It was as if she came out of nowhere; I somehow didn't even think to ask where Patrick and Ben's parents were the night before, but they were definitely around now. "Should we stop?" I asked, rather hoping I could keep going (and that he'd continue to jerk me off while I did it). Ben, however, released me from his clutches and nodded, not saying anything as he stepped off his bed to find his clothes.

"Well," I said, putting my pants back on. "Thanks for inviting me over." I quietly opened his bedroom door and made a dash for the front door, trying to remember the layout of the home, hoping that I would not run into Ben's mother. (I did, of course, not run; while it may have ensured that I'd get out of there faster, it would be too obvious, like if you were running to the bathroom in the mall—you don't want to bring that sort of attention to yourself.)

I sped home and quickly changed into my uniform—dark green Dickies work pants and a tan Dickies shirt (all I was missing, really, was the park ranger's hat). I ignored my mother's questions about "the party," rushing out the door to make it to work on time. I couldn't tell if I was just hungover or still drunk; either way, I didn't want to spend eight hours outside in the humidity that settled on the shore of the Potomac River.

I worked at the boathouse, because the guy who usually worked there was on vacation. I sat there in what was basically a shed with a counter and cash register, hoping to God that the river would be choppy enough so that I could avoid dragging the large, heavy paddleboats down from the seawall to the beach. Luckily it was a slow day, so I spent the majority of my shift laying my throbbing head on the sandy counter, occasionally stirring when I heard one of my managers drive by in their ranger trucks.

The events from the night (and the morning) floated through my mind like a film montage. I watched myself rolling around naked on the bed with Ben to the soundtrack provided by Ryan Adams. I got hard thinking about it again, wondering if it was a one-time thing or if it would happen again. While getting a blowjob was certainly nice, I wasn't so sure about giving one, and maybe this was just that experimental phase in which I realize that I'm only attracted to a man if he happens to be sucking my dick.

Of course, this did not stop me from thinking about going down on Ben again that night during my daily routine of drinking a Zima and masturbating.

I IMed with Ben a few times in the next couple of weeks, but we never discussed what happened or the significance of it; the closest we got was sharing links to gay porn websites. The fantasy of having a summer fling became less realistic, and I realized the most important thing about a random gay hook-up: it usually doesn't happen a second time, much less develop into a regular thing. This is especially true of your first few times, particularly if you're not really sure about what it all means. You feel too fucking weird about it to ever want to see or talk to the guy ever again. Within two weeks the brief IMs with Ben had tapered off. And then I discovered the bump on my balls.

It was a normal weekday night: everyone had gone to bed and I had connected to the reliably slow Internet to begin browsing Yahoo chat rooms for masturbatory material. As I began chatting with some anonymous character, I slid my hand into my boxer briefs. I suddenly felt something on my balls—it wasn't there before, and it certainly felt weird. More than weird, it sort of stung when I touched it. My stomach immediately dropped and sweat started to build up on my forehead, as if I had found a switch on my scrotum that triggered anxiety and hypochondria. I jumped out of my desk chair and bent the snakelike lamp upside down so I could see what I was feeling. Sure enough, there was a bump: a little red thing that was already growing to a head. I felt flushed and sat back down in my seat, and I immediately shut down the Yahoo chat room, leaving some poor gay boy in the middle of his predictable cybersex routine.

I did what any rational person would do: I grabbed my health textbook (which the university bookstore conveniently did not buy back) and flipped to the unit focusing on sexual health so that I could diagnose myself. I found a chart that listed every sexually transmitted infection, scanning the symptoms to figure out what I had caught. I limited it to three options: herpes, genital warts, and chancroid. I immediately searched the Internet for pictures of each and convinced myself that the most likely culprit was chancroid, which can begin to flare up just weeks after sexual contact. I read that the bump usually results in a painful ulcer, and I decided that I had to go to the doctor immediately.

I knew, of course, that stealthily getting an appointment at the local clinic was impossible, as I grew up in the kind of small town in which no one could keep a secret. Once in seventh grade my parents found out I had failed a math test because my teacher stopped by our house during her nightly power-walk around our neighborhood. I also wasn't sure who to see; I had been going to my pediatrician up until my college physical, and his office was an hour away in the closest city. I knew I had to tell my parents, and in my hypochondriatic panic I wrote a note and left it in front of my parents' bedroom door so that one of them would talk to me in the morning before they left for work. "Please come wake me up before you leave in the morning," I wrote. "I need to talk to you about something." I managed to calm myself down enough to get in bed with the help of two Zimas, but I spent the majority of that sleepless night fearing that I could never have sex with anyone ever because I now had an incurable disease, all because I was stupid enough to get a blowjob.

My mother woke me up the next morning. "Is everything okay?" she asked. I immediately began to shake and, close to tears, delivered the news.

"Um, I think I may have something."

"What does that mean? Have what?"

"An STD, I think."

She stared at me, silently. "I haven't had sex," I said, as if hearing that your son had only gotten a BJ was some sort of consolation. "It's only happened once. But now I have a bump on my testicles." (One uses the clinical term when sharing such news with family, I assumed.)

"You didn't pay for it, did you?" she asked with an accusatory look.

"What?! No!" I squealed, immediately more embarrassed by the notion that my mother could imagine that I had gone to a prostitute for a blowjob.

"Was it with a boy?"

"No," I lied, deciding it wasn't the best time to admit that I was, in fact, a bit more interested in fucking guys than girls. "It was a girl, a friend of mine from school."

"Well, you need to make an appointment today," she said, curtly. "Try to get in before you go to work. I believe Dr. Jenkins's office opens at nine." With that, she left the room.

I'm not sure what is worse: telling your mother that you may have an STD, or realizing for the first time that she is incredibly disappointed. For all she knew, I spent my first year at college dipping my balls in any mouth that held itself open for their receipt. I did not care to tell her that this was my first time, and that all but one of my orgasms were self-inflicted and my teabagging experience was incredibly limited.

I got an appointment for later that morning, and I called the park to let them know I'd be late to work. I drove about a mile to the health center, parked in the back, and ran in quickly, as if getting there as fast as possible was going to speed up the process of finding out that I would be ruined for the rest of my life. I was luckily the only person in the waiting room, but I realized as I filled out my paperwork that I had graduated from high school with the receptionist. She wasn't anyone I knew very well; we didn't have classes together. The only thing I knew about her was how many guys she slept with in high school. She probably didn't have chancroid.

After filling out the paperwork I followed the nurse into the examination room. She took my vitals as I sat there silently, trying not to squirm so much to avoid tearing the sheet of protective paper covering the padded examination table. Finally, she asked what brought me to the doctor.

"Um, I have a bump on my testicles."

She nonchalantly handed me a paper gown and told me to undress, assuring me that Dr. Jenkins would be in to see me shortly. I then spent forty excruciating minutes in the room with my bare ass on that papered exam table waiting for the doctor, the informational pamphlets ("What is the flu?" "So You've Got Mono!") and the paralyzing fear of my soon-to-be-diagnosed incurable disease the only things keeping me occupied. I wondered how this would affect me. Would I ever have sex again? Would I have to join an online community specifically for those afflicted with chancroid? Would I ever be able to tell my friends? Would I have to tell Ben about what he did to me?

There was a knock on the door. Dr. Jenkins walked in with my file. "Hello, Tyler," she said with the surprising familiarity of someone whom I had never met, which I suppose was a comfortable put-on for her considering she walked into rooms where strangers waited for her in bare-assed paper gowns.

"What brings you in today?" she asked without making eye contact and while grabbing latex gloves and long cotton swabs from a storage container on the counter on the other side of the room. "Well," I started, "I have a bump..."

She didn't even let me finish before raising up the bottom of the gown and grabbing my balls with her chilly, gloved hand. I could feel her press the Q-Tip directly on the bump, and I tried to look over the paper—which she was holding up between us—in order to see her reaction and assess how bad off I was. She lowered the gown and began to take off her gloves, dropping them in the trash with the Q-Tip.

"Are you outside a lot this summer?" she asked. I was confused by the question. Was she wondering if I was having a great time playing outside with friends? Or was she suggesting that I had contracted chancroid from a highway rest stop or a public park?

"Uh, I'm working at the park this summer," I stammered, "so I'm outside for most of the day."

"Ah," she said. "Well, the humidity can cause acne, but you don't appear to have any other major problems with it. I don't think it's worth giving you a prescription for it; it'll probably go away in a couple of days."

"Wait, what?"

"The pimple. It's probably painful given the area, but I don't think giving you something for it with make it clear up any quicker."

"Oh."

And with that good news I tore myself out of the paper gown and back into my regular clothes, signed the paperwork which would send the co-pay bill to my parents (thanks, Mom!), and walked out of the clinic with the contentedness that comes with being STD-free. That night I cracked open a celebratory Zima, excited to learn at eighteen that you can, in fact, get pimples on your balls, and they were far less stressful than the occasional blowjob.

Some Thoughts on the Crapper

Originally published in Gawk, a now-extinct Internet magazine, 1997.

Jonathan Ames

THIS MORNING I WOKE UP WITH A GOOD-SIZED ERECTION. I was next to my girlfriend and the slight contact of her leg caused this to happen. My girlfriend likes it when I have a morning erection. She likes my penis. She says it's fat. Not long, but fat.

For my taste it's too pink and rather ugly. My girlfriend once saw a thickly muscled, whitish-pink dog, the kind that has small eyes and was once used in a beer commercials, and she said, "That dog looks like your penis." I objected, though secretly I concurred. I also think that I see things on my penis and a doctor friend of mine told me that all men have skin-plaque on their penises. I'd like to dip my penis in some flossing-mouthwash solution and remove that plaque. Actually that's not a bad idea. Johnson and Johnson, which has a fitting name, should come up with some sort of penis-wash that removes penis-plaque. Johnson-Wash. It's a winning name.

Unfortunately, one of the points of this essay is that I almost dipped my penis in the toilet bowl this morning. I had my morning erection, as I mentioned above, but I also had to take my morning crap. Lately my bowels have been regular and good because I was taking these herb and psyllium tablets, but generally my digestion is poor. Though I try to take my own advice, which I once gave to a semi-constipated girlfriend: "Be grateful for whatever comes out." I dispense this advice, because if you know anything about health, you know how essential and vital it is to get the waste out of us. Detoxify at all costs.

So this morning I walked into the bathroom and was worried about my erection. I tried to do a yoga breath to make my penis wilt. Men will understand why I needed my cock to go down, but women might not know that you can't have a bowel movement if you have a hard-on. Hard-ons take precedence over everything. They override all functions. It's Darwinism at play.

So if you don't let your erection wilt completely what happens is that when you sit on the toilet and push your cock down into the bowl to piss, you get erect again. At least I do. The pushing down must excite me, even though I don't want to be excited. So I really need to let my cock go down, but I'm almost always too impatient to let the thing deflate completely and I end up with a big erection just when I need to shit and then things get quite complicated. I really am an idiot. I never learn. I make the same mistakes over and over again in life. Don't fall in love with people who psychologically resemble your parents—yet I do it every time. Don't drink alcohol, you're alcoholic—yet every couple of years or months or days, I think I can handle a drink. Don't try to take a shit when you're semierect, you'll wreak havoc—and yet I do it every time. It happened this morning. I was semierect and hoped that this time it would be different. I pushed my penis down toward the water to piss before shitting (a necessary order of events) and the thing became rebelliously erect again. I was presented with my usual problems.

My cock expanded, and the head of my penis was speeding for the underlip of the bowl, where all sorts of horrible microorganisms and stray pubic hairs collect. And this was my girlfriend's toilet, which she shares with her roommate—*a man*! I knew that all sorts of this weird stuff was caught in that underlip. So just before my growing cock kissed that lip, I hurriedly pointed it down, but then it skimmed the germ-infested water, which was at high tide. Why is life so insane? I then yanked my wet-with-toilet-water cock straight up, but by now I was in danger if I pissed of having urine hit me in the face. So I took my cock, like a gearshift, and sought a compromise position: I skirted the very top of the cold water and aimed the nozzle to shoot at a target just below the toilet tip. I let the urine flow. I hoped my aim would be true, that I would fire just below the lip and not shoot over the edge and splatter against the wall. This was a real worry, because when I piss out of an erection my accuracy goes down markedly. I'm like a shotgun when erect—I scatter fire.

But disaster was averted. The urine stayed in the bowl. I was able to relax now, and my penis went down. It was blessedly soft. So then my sphincter relaxed—a kind of chain reaction—and I was able to release my bowels. But how tawdry life is. Why must I shit? I have to remember, though, that we all defecate. I think it would be very helpful to people if we saw movie stars going to the bathroom. Self-esteem across the nation would skyrocket.

But since there are no public service announcements of this sort, I was shitting and worrying like crazy about the noises I was making, the wheezing of gas that was going on. I was terribly frightened that my girlfriend had awakened and was listening to me—her room is right next to the toilet and the walls are paper thin—so I hurried my bowel movement. I then flushed, got off the can, and while washing my hands I realized that I wasn't finished. I had double-clutched my shit. I hate when this happens. I'm so anxious to get it over with that I rush and then flush and think I'm done, but I'm not. Then the person outside the toilet hears me crap again and flush again and they can't believe what's going on in there. You see, whatever toilet I'm on someone is always listening to me and feeling loathing for me—when it comes to shitting I'm afraid I have some paranoid schizophrenic tendencies, but only in this one area. Anyway, a double-clutch on the toilet means double the time in the bathroom and double the embarrassment. But things can actually get worse: there's always the fear, which is sometimes realized, that the second flush won't work so soon after the first flush. Then you have to wait for the tank to refill—like waiting for your cock to go down; patience, you idiot!—and flush a *third time*!

Well, I sat back down on the toilet this morning, finished my movement, felt like a fool, flushed again (it worked), washed the hands again, and returned to my girlfriend's room. She was still asleep. It was only eight o'clock in the morning, and I had already been to war.

I crawled back into bed and masturbated a little to soothe myself after my nightmarish start to my day. My girlfriend woke up a few minutes later and reached for my cock. She held on to it like a pacifier and said in a sleepy voice, "I love how you're so erect in the morning."

I didn't let her know that this was an artificial morning erection, nor did I tell her what I had been through. This is an example of human isolation. We can never fully be known. But it's better that way. Why puncture her happiness by revealing to her the hell of my inner life? It might be her only dose of joy all day long. She squeezed my cock tight. "I love it," she said sweetly.

"I know," I said. "I know you love it."

Julian

Charlotte Shane

THE FIRST WORDS I HEARD HIM SPEAK suggested that I was a writer. We were riding on the subway, me seated, him standing. My face was shiny with sweat because of the long walk to the metro and I wore a pale green dress that was not the right color for my skin. In spite of this, I had the bizarre sense that I was very attractive to everyone I passed and so when he spoke to me I was not surprised, although strangers rarely talk to other strangers in this city.

He told me I looked like a columnist for one of the local papers and I didn't recognize her name but confirmed that I wrote. This was very bold, if not an outright lie, since I hadn't written any poetry in over a year and recently dropped out of my second Masters program with no connections and no published texts, academic or otherwise.

My stop turned out to be his stop. We rode the escalator to the sidewalk and stood a little longer, talking. I gave my number while my boyfriend watched from his car. He was twice as old as I was, so calling him my boyfriend always felt strange, but we'd been having sex for two and half years by that point and lived together. He was picking me up so we could go grocery shopping.

Later—not much later, just a few hours after—my boyfriend said, "when I saw you two together, I thought that you and I shouldn't be." In less than a month, we wouldn't.

•

The fourth or fifth time I saw Julian was in his office at the end of the day, with his coworkers gone and the space our own so we could dry hump and make out on the desks. By this time, I'd promised my boyfriend I wouldn't have sex with Julian again, so I gave a blowjob instead. This was the second time I tasted his semen. The first was the first night we had sex, and it didn't last very long because I stopped him, and went down on him until he came. It all happened on the couch downstairs in my home. Both Julian and I were very drunk.

It was in his office, though, where he told me he'd never had anal sex. His cock was very large, but anal was so trendy and ubiquitous that I thought it impossible that there was anyone left in America who hadn't tried it. It's strange to think of what might had occurred between us afterward if he'd not told me this. I was incredibly taken with the idea of being someone's first, probably because my boyfriend had done almost everything at least once and done it years ago, when he was my age. Julian's newness was powerfully sexy, and although we were both twenty-four, I tend to remember myself as being several years his senior.

•

I'd been afraid he wouldn't even call me, not because he seemed cruel or insincere but because maybe he put the number in incorrectly or lost his phone. I was terrified at the thought that there might be no way for us to find each other again, but he did call and he said he was about to leave to go to a bar with his friends.

I wanted to join Julian at the bar. I wanted to see him drink a beer, I wanted to know how he held the glass neck with his fingers and I wanted to see him with his friends. I wanted to be with him in every situation and every circumstance. But weekends were for my boyfriend and me, and there was no graceful way to exit our Saturday ennui.

I was gone anyway, of course. My curiosity made me frantic. After only ten minutes together, Julian's mere existence had sown necessary chaos in my world. When I rode the metro again, alone, I stared out the black windows and pictured his face.

♦

Although we both were swept away in the tide of each other, there was no talk of a committed relationship. Too many factors were in the way, not least of which was the vague nature of the rest of the world when we were cocooned in one another's company. I only saw his house once, during his going-away party. He drank more than I and after the guests left and the housemates retired to their rooms, we ended up on the couch together.

"Say something," he said. He called me by my name.

"Say what?" I asked.

"It's never been like this."

"You want me to say that?"

"Only if you mean it," he sighed, keeping his eyes closed. "It's never been exactly like this." He had beautiful full lips, swollen lips.

He asked me to go with him on his trip to London, but it was too late to make the plans. That didn't matter. I felt like I'd already dreamed the trip we would have had, that I'd been back from it for weeks, still glowing.

I missed him very much while he was away. I found myself saying to my boyfriend, "You know one thing about Julian that I really like?" It would come out of nowhere, while I was walking outside and looking at a torn billboard or doing laundry or watching TV. I wasn't trying to be mean to my boyfriend. At that time I still felt close to him, and so, as with a friend, I wanted to share with him the things that excited me. I think he knew that trying to keep me from seeing Julian at all was an impossibility, so he tried to impose a ban on Julian and I having sex, as in sexual intercourse. I claimed that this was unreasonable. And so he said, "No anal sex. I couldn't stand it if you had anal sex with him." My boyfriend was the first man I had anal sex with. And he may have thought at that time that he was the only, but he would have been mistaken.

•

Julian took me to his childhood home, where I met both of his parents as well as his younger brother. We took his dog on a walk through the woods until we reached a giant field where groups of Latino men played soccer, and then we turned around and went back to his house. Julian's parents were still married, happily so, although his father's heart was breaking because Julian's mother was very sick with cancer. She didn't seem sick. She seemed warm and momlike and I wanted her to approve of me, but she was going through that cycle when even being well starts to seem like still being very sick, only not suffering quite so much. His younger brother was too young to be sexy to me, although he was very good looking and had dark hair. This detail amused me because Julian was pure blond everywhere, with dandelion fuzz for eyelashes and glimmering gold pubic hair.

We slid into the attic bed naked on a different night, while there was nobody home. I brought lube up even though we somehow left our clothes on a lower floor, because I knew that what I wanted most out of my life then was Julian's cock in my ass. He lay on his back and watched as I fingered my asshole to relax and warm up the tight ring of muscle. I was probably wet from our lazy making out on the couch downstairs or simply from being near him and feeling the planes of his body. He had a cock like a tube, evenly thick down the whole column, and I made him stay still as I lowered myself down on it very slowly, shaking. It was so wide, and not just wide but long. It took a great deal of deliberate effort to make it fit. He asked about my trembling and I wasn't sure how to explain it except to say that one of my friends said it happened to her every time she had anal, but I didn't remember it ever happening to me. We looked into each other's faces while I moved up and down and his eyes were my only reminder that I was human, hunched though I was like an animal in some situation it didn't comprehend.

When we switched to all fours, Julian's eagerness overcame him and he fucked me too hard. "Slowly!" I'd say. "Not so deep!" But he seemed incapable of listening, too fascinated by watching his pubic bone meet my ass cheeks to hold himself in check. So there was pain but pain through the sieve of intense pleasure, and my cunt was a well of wetness, so swollen and soaked my fingers could barely find traction. There were almost certainly tears when I was facing away from him like this and so buffeted by sensation I did not have the presence of mind to manage or stop it. He came in my ass with unmistakable relief. He'd only ever come inside my mouth before because I was no longer on the pill.

I don't remember being angry at him for not being more careful with me then, but it may have been part of the reason I felt so guiltless about being careless with him after he was gone. He wrote me long emails that went unanswered; I didn't pick up the phone when he called. At some point, even before that night, I realized all the dizzy euphoria of our first weeks wouldn't be sustainable for me. I would be left better once he was gone, better for having known him. He would think of me more than I thought of him.

I'm not sure that any of his memories could rival the intensity of mine, of the tableau of him starting the shower afterward, both of us naked and shivering now because of the cold. He had an exceptionally lean body, so thin that he was troubled by it but it thrilled me because it was unlike any of the myriad male bodies I encountered through work. He was broad and flat, practically two-dimensional, with a stomach that is almost solely the domain of young men. Running my fingers over his torso, with his muscled grooves like ripples in water, I was in awe. And then again, watching him bend coltishly to fiddle with the taps, there came a surge of wonder. I was not in love with him, but it was something close, something woven with gratitude and delight and ease. Being with him was so easy in spite of the fact that all the ways I could think to describe his effect were violent. "He kicked me awake," I wrote once. "He was the crowbar that pried open my life."

Our last time we had sex was outside on a park bench with the monument across the lake in front of us like the artless, inelegant metaphor it is. I sat on his lap and pulled up my blue dress, the skin of my thighs even more pale in the moonlight. At one point he said, "kiss me," so I lay back on his chest and turned my head while I squirmed. I loved the noises he made while he was inside me. They were short, whimpering little breaths, almost like he was crying, begging even. He came into his own hands, practically throwing my hips up to lift me off himself in time, and I licked and bit his wet fingertips while he sat, dazed, until finally saying something that made both of us laugh very hard for a long time. I can't remember what it was. At my offering, he wiped his hands on my sweater and then we walked back up the slope to his car.

In the next few years, he would lose the dream job for which he was relocating. His mother would pass away from her cancer. He would move back to the city where we met and I still lived. But I wouldn't find this last part out until looking him up online because writing this made me think of his pretty, full name. I contacted him once, and his response was angry. *Why did you abandon me?* was essentially what he wanted to know. *If I let you back into my life, will you abandon me again?* It made me very uncomfortable, and I wrote some angrily awkward response that said, essentially, yes.

All of the now-knowledge makes that last night intensely poignant, but at the time it probably felt far simpler. Of course I can't know for sure what was in his heart, and we were both sad that he was leaving, but I imagine we mostly felt the way we always did when we were together: happy.

Julian and I ate together at a Thai restaurant once, and I was unusually candid, more aware of the rest of my life than I usually was when with him. "What do you call something that shows up unannounced, screws everything up, then leaves?" I asked. We couldn't come up with the right word. I wonder now which one of us would have found the term more useful.

Libertad

Erica Moore

THERE WERE FOUR YEARS between this trip and the last time I saw you.

Between this trip and our last afternoon in a Florida panhandle park in the glary, trashy southern sun. We said goodbye, and we wouldn't admit it for weeks, but I knew it was not the goodbye of long-distance lovers; it was a shrug and a giving up. And I kissed you and cried in this costumey discount sundress I never wore again. Accepted your monogrammed handkerchief like alms under coves of Spanish moss and tried not to stain your dress whites. I cried most of the way to visit distant grandparents, three hours down melting asphalt in a rental car, because I was leaving American soil, and you were busy being groomed. Because surely, this sensible disappointment was how stories ended.

The second time I saw you again—all these years later—I came obediently to the other side of the country. Flew to visit you in another sunny city you hated, still the only cultured Jew around. I came to town again this time at your invitation, but so much more reluctantly. I'd sent an awkward series of texts earlier in the week, in line for coffee, clarifying that I was coming but was so far from ready to sleep with anyone else.

With someone.

I was still in those early post-break-up months of shifting plurals and titles, unexpectedly finished with the man that had held my ground in the years between you and me. Still in those days where any laugh morphed halfway into something wetter and more broken. There were no words that couldn't remind me. And yet, how many weeks of relational shivah can pass before that disloyal thought arises: possibilities remain.

And so I came.

The first night I followed you from your old Subaru up in to your new bedroom, foreign as a hotel. Worn down after the layover and flight, unsure if this was the guest room. Not really caring if I was misleading you by going where you led. I fell on to your enormous white bed—white duvet, white sheets, four white pillows. Tried to remember if you'd always been so particular. You crawled in, too, and I think we laid beside each other for a while. Just talking in low voices and then not talking while a fan oscillated air over our covered bodies, exotic again and polarized.

I wandered out several times, escaping into your cold apartment that felt like a farmhouse or a penitentiary: comfortless. I was regretful on your hard wood floors, in your quiet empty bathroom. One a.m. on a Friday night and none of your words sounded familiar, and I rebuked myself: What did I think I'd find here? I sat on your humid balcony for a while, watching palm trees waltz in the dark, choked back tears that didn't make any sense, and willed the stars to lecture me. Worked not to cry in the dark and came back to bed. Where else could I be?

Of course, two days later—two days into a Mexican road trip and the desert sun and rebirth, I'd be half in love with you again. Half in love with your hand on my warm thigh, pushing skirts away like nuisance children, and your easy laugh and your open car window and your freedom. But that night, it was all still nearly strangers, purgatory reheated.

So I came back to bed, or maybe you came and took me there. Lay back down beside you like waters tested. And at some point, the plate tectonics of old love took over. I rolled to my side, slipped my ass backward to you just enough to balance want with dignity. Because let me admit it: I was born to be cusped. And you interpreted every passive signal as it was sent, shored up behind me dutifully. Into this perfect space.

I had forgotten that. We've said that nearly embarrassing line before, haven't we all—about perfect fits? But maybe to only one or two men. And yes, I had thought it about you in the years between us: That we fit together as though once pulled apart. Reunited. Okay, simpler: that we fit together and fucked together like people do not usually.

The thing about you that night was that I could hear the want so thick in your voice. You—*always unshakeable, unwanting, casual*—suddenly undone. By me.

Of course your hands were everywhere, but slowed. So fucking careful, like I wasn't already broken. Big and rougher than mine, on hipbones, with such a low, small sound I almost didn't hear it. Then driving up the side of my hip, up under my shirt. And each inch of skin must have taken ten minutes to traverse. An hour. The first new hand on my stomach in more than three years. But it was just the side of your hand. The long yoga line of one finger to wrist, brushing from the curve of my belly, tracing up my ribs. Smoothing out goose bumps, plowing anticipation. And then you stopped, just below my breasts even as my elbow came swinging in slowly like a lazy goalie to block your next attempt.

But then you said this, you reasoned, *I just want this place, okay? This place is mine.*

And you slipped one finger under the chin of my bra to demonstrate—not greedy enough for breasts. Just resting in the valley between. That was the goal. This inch-wide span of flesh over breastplate. This funny bony expanse between two objects that alternately earn my love and dissatisfaction. You just pressed one finger there, slid up and down once like water in this land between, made a hushed noise I heard for an hour.

The idea that you had wanted to get back there—*back to this specific, inconsequential place that I suppose only I had ever taken time to admire*—for four years killed me.

We kept that pose for a long time and you let me talk about the breakup and how left and unchosen I felt. How off kilter. Months later I'd walk with you to a different conclusion that involved less love lost and more the mourning of expectations. Of control. But tonight, you just listened—sweet and reassuring and willing to hold all these topics of friendship—and didn't tease when those fevered tears fell on to your hands, made Rorschach blots on your clean white sheets. You smoothed my hair back over and over, which only made me cry harder, and those tears ran down through my hairline, into my own ears like ice dams melted.

You listened, hard behind me, until I quieted. And then those wet hands slipped down from the crown of my head that you held like a hat, patient and undeterred back to my hip. Returned to the waistband of my flannel shorts, and yes they dove down. It's hard to recount it now without it suggesting manipulation, but it wasn't that at all. I didn't know how far I wanted your hands to go just yet, but I knew so fucking much that I needed to want again. To be wanted. Pressed against me, I could feel you so hard I wondered if it hurt a little. You apologized, and I smiled too small for you to see. Thought about you always so hard; your miraculous severity.

In a long pause of words, in a moment of just breath in a dark room, you slid up from the south. Drew one hand up the curve of my ass, up into the leg of my shorts, just beneath the line where my panties met soft inner thigh. Just to that sweetest, softest plane of flesh that I could commission to have stroked all day by the right hands.

We didn't sleep together that night, but you slipped in, under the line of my black boy- shorts—*halfway between getting-laid-panties and not-getting-laid panties*—and back into four years of wetness. Like this sensible part of me alone had been waiting for you in the backyard while my head entertained nostalgia and pride and habit in the formal sitting room up front.

You slipped your fingers in, halfway, and brought them back to your mouth. I loved you for that. Kissed you for that, tasting this revived version of myself on you and remembering all the prudish men that came before. I said No that night, not ready to be anything to you yet. But wanting you, remembering how I had wanted you in dark nights over the bay of years between us. You took your hand and the smell of me and left the room, came back self-appeased and hard again within ten minutes. I lay in the dark, thinking about you grasping yourself tight, sliding up and down, and I wished I'd seen it. Wished I'd had the mettle to say yes when you'd asked if you could come in the bed beside me. Understood why I'd said no.

I rolled over and stretched my fingers out on your bare chest, through the hair, across the broadest place I know. After five minutes you told me you didn't actually like it, *Why would I want to be petted?* you asked, and I flushed with humiliation, rolled away from you, and let the fan cool my face. Hid my face and thought about how much I dislike artificially moved air and your white noise. Later, still awake, I decided it was invigorating to hear the truth, to know straight away what you wanted and what you didn't. Remembered that your honesty was always my favorite thing. I scooted back to touch the top of your foot with just the heel of mine and finally fell asleep beside you.

We left that privileged city the next morning and drove south across the border with day-trippers and night workers going home. Stopped in TJ for *Seguros De Autos*, stopped for roadside ceviche, stopped for brown-bagged beers we drank in the car, stopped to admire cliffs like Greece, rising out of nowhere.

It was halfway through the trip until we walked up to that midnight when I pulled you in, sudden and rough, for more. Felt you so, so present, back inside me in the marital bed of a Baja inn hung with imperial colors, armored with heavy woods and crucifixes. Four years gone like wood to ash and I think I cried again, for the newness of it. And then I didn't. Then I knotted my legs up and around your back, high and tight as strangulation. Put your hands on my ass and reminded you how to lift my hips while you pushed down in to them just as far as you could. Maybe like you did four years back. Wondered, for a moment, if that was too much to ask. *How do you pull me to you and push me away and balance yourself through it all?* I wondered. Decided you owed me, life owed me that much, and stopped worrying.

Later, closer to daybreak, you turned me over and closed my legs tight. Laid down on me like finishing a sentence and slid deep inside what has never been more aquatic. You come this way almost every time and I feel like a mermaid, like some exotic Victorian cripple. Legs crossed tight, squeezing you and waiting for your breathing to change, for that moment where your voice and your breath would rattle together. I sifted through the vibrations for the confessions that drift between them some nights. Pushing my back and ass up in to you, turning my neck for your mouth to find. Burning all the skin off wounded elbows I never notice until work meetings the next week. Waiting for you to crack open and moan like you never do except in those moments. For you to push your hands down over mine, splayed on the bed before us and I'll arch my fingers backward into your palm, red and shaking, like these hands are fucking, too.

Was this night the start of my infatuation with the almost-fucking? With you hard outside me, poised. I would climb on top of you in that carefree country. Sit on your lap, one long leg on each side of you. Hips and thighs softer and paler than I might prefer, but sexier for being displayed on you. Lean back and grab the wide tip of you, slide it across me, through these tiny cupped hands, these two soft lips, this southern mouth wet with mischief. Up and down like a bow on custom made strings.

Don't torture me, you'd say, your voice thick and caught. And I'd smile, crooked, with my eyes closed and wouldn't listen. *You have tortured me enough*, I'd think, *you can do this for me now.*

You should understand that we can't tell you how good this feels. This moment before you conquer and claim. The moment before you blink. Where you drift and rub and pull back and slide forward in friction that feels like not breathing; Not in to me but past me, not owning me. Without permission to own me.

And maybe all of that is nothing compared to the second when you have had enough and on the backslide you change angles, indiscernibly. And you drive in. And I let you fall in. To this flesh inside me that is not of this world. That is molded of heart and guts and radio transmitters and fingertips and feels the slide and entering and filling of me like a scream.

We spent the second half of that weekend in beds farther south, relearning synchronization and the places swollen lips fit and the distraction of want so urgent it borders on anger. Noting each other's evolutions and trying to remember, *had we liked it like this before?* until it didn't matter, because we liked it like this now, and we squeezed eyes tight and cried out hollow nonsensical sounds into open clumsy mouths. And then we lay chastely afterward in that spent gloaming, in the breeze that smelled of eucalyptus and high desert and dying aquatic life. Talked slowly about the things we never admitted the first time around, *not even under that glary panhandle sun*. But really, never said it all.

We didn't know it yet, but we'd spend the rest of the year with no promises or requests in strange cities, in the first sweet fucking after I saw you again which was better than charity, better than children, better than liquor.

But at the end of that first weekend, you just deposited me at a hot airport in a southern city. I watched you drive away with a wink and didn't know what to do with any of this. Didn't yet know how to hold just something. So I walked inside to ticketing with my black bag rolling behind me like the question of whether to cry or laugh.

And then I smiled behind my sunglasses; wet already and thinking of power restored.

From Milwaukee With Love

Halle Kiefer

ON OCTOBER 3, 1849, EDGAR ALLEN POE COLLAPSED in front Ryan's Saloon in Baltimore, delirious and calling for water that he could not drink. At one point in my life, I was pretty sure we would have that in common. While most historians blame Poe's death on run-of-the-mill writer-killers like alcoholism or TB, another theory points to a culprit that I grew up learning to fear more than serial killers: rabies. Now, with regard to my own life, alcoholism is the way more likely killer in my Irish Catholic family (we have big flabby slow hearts and don't usually play with animals who are foaming at the mouth), but since we lived in a rural area in Ohio, it certainly wasn't the one we heard about at the kitchen table, forks poised halfway to our mouths as our parents told us horror stories about a kid (one who was just like us) who had found an adorable, weepy-eyed baby possum staggering around the yard in the middle of the day. For weeks, months, years even, this little girl or boy would be playing and laughing, enjoying their apparent health and functioning limbs and ability to swallow, when all of the sudden they'd be hit by paralysis, hydrophobia, and insanity. Death. A bite, a surface scratch, even saliva on your hands was a potential killer.

I'd give our toothless, grinning dachshund the side eye as she lolled grinning in her leopard-print dog bed. I slid my feet up underneath me. You could never be too sure.

Four years and four hundred miles away, I lived in the virtually wild animal-free borough of Brooklyn. Even the dogs were smaller over here! My childhood fear of rabies had fluttered up into some dark cobweb-covered corner of my subconscious, sleeping soundly next to other adolescent gross-out terrors like lice, ringworm, and tetanus. I had other, bigger horrors lined up for me: mouth-drying existential dread, epic student loans, a Craigslist apartment where baby cockroaches flowed out of the kitchen sink and a machete fight in the hall left blood smeared on the bricks outside. Park Slope was not exactly shaping up like I had imagined.

So I did what any neurotic, baby-fatted country girl (does it still count as baby fat at twenty-three?) would do in this situation: I started Internet dating. I cannot stress enough what a horrible idea this was. I'm not saying that Internet dating is a bad idea but—yes, yes, of course I am, I'm saying that Internet dating is a nightmarishly terrible idea. I'm sure plenty of people have really great reasons for doing it (agoraphobia; living on an oil rig) but most people are using online dating sites when they really should be trying to fix whatever is compelling them to use dating sites (abject despair; grad school). Which is how I found myself in the kitchen of a sweltering railroad apartment in the lap of a guy I didn't know all that well; a satyr of man with a bike and bottles of prescription drugs that he didn't actually need and an ass that looked like two balloons held aloft by two strings, and if you followed the strings they stretched all the way up to heaven, where the ends were being held by God himself, and God is winking at you. He was clever, vaguely dangerous, and powerfully beautiful. We sat in his kitchen, my head on his chest and the summer heat and smell of Marlboro Menthols with the sharp smell of his t-shirt worn for days on end made me cross-eyed with lust, loopy with lowered inhibitions. I closed my eyes, and we kissed. He pulled back and smiled, rubbing his hands along my back as he started to smile, "Hey, did I mention that I got bit by a dog last week?"

I saw the gleaming thread of saliva that stretched between our lips and my heart seized up and I stifled a Charlie Brown–style *AAAAAAAARGH*. Of course I contracted rabies. I had come all this way to the city, the concrete jungle, to live in an environment almost completely devoid of wildlife, only to have the lurking death follow me here. I was in a stranger's kitchen in a new city, lured in by the stifling heat and the crazy-making smell of him and the underlying promise that I might be able to get my hands on a naked body that wasn't my own, and of course this is what happens. Then the guy started to go out about some PLAY he was writing, like we were even going to LIVE that long, when I interrupted him. "You could have rabies," I told him, "You could have just given me rabies." He laughed kindly, foolishly, saying, "Oh please. If I just gave you rabies, then I have bigger problems. Like the fact that I would have rabies!" Which was pretty inaccurate, given that I was going to tear that place apart. Physically I was frozen, but mentally I was already swinging a floor lamp into his television. You want to see crazy? I'll show you Cujo! Did I mention it was a homeless person's dog that bit him? Not that homeless people consort with rabid dogs (that's nothing but a vicious stereotype!), but if a man and his dog slept in the park overnight, they would probably expose themselves to all sorts of animals like fox kits and coyote puppies and god knows what other little teeny harbingers of disease that romp in the night. As his hand moved down my back and he leaned up to rub his beard against my clenched, furious jaw, the thin reedy voice of my neurosis (played by one Mr. Woody Allen), who had just been shrieking for me to proceed immediately to the nearest emergency room, suddenly sounded strangely distant, pushed into a well or locked in the supply closet of my mind. My animal brain had already shaken itself awake and was wagging its tail, drooling, and I followed it, moving ahead toward his bed like a St. Bernard blundering into a hidden bat-filled cave. Given the circumstances, I reasoned, I should probably do my best to live it up before the brain damage set in.

Maybe it already had. As soon as I left his place the next day, I felt my pupils contract painfully in the bright August sun. I had the distinct urge to hiss and scuttle up into some kind of belfry. Suddenly my arms felt so fatigued lifting my 30-pound-purse, my throat slow to swallow as I ate an entire sleeve of Saltines. My malaise moved from pathological to pathogen in my mind, and, like every illness ever, my fatigue at the end of the workday took on new meaning. I pictured the last terrible days in the throes of madness: the modest yet deeply moving funeral, the tasteful musical tributes, the inevitable, hushed whispers about how I had contracted such an unusual disease. "Boning," my poor relatives would whisper, "she caught it while boning." During the hours of frantic Googling that filled the next week, I discovered that, once symptoms of rabies have set in, the only way anyone has ever survived the illness is via the Milwaukee Protocol (YOU DIDN'T KNOW THIS?!?!? Please quickly finish this story, put a five-dollar bill into a stamped envelope and mail it to me, then go to Wikipedia and look it up!).

In 2005, doctors essentially put a fifteen-year-old girl into suspended animation for a month, and she survived. "Don't worry," my far-too-calm mother assured me when I called her, "we'll have them put you in a chemical-induced coma for sure." At least there are people left in this world who understand me. I made her promise to take out my contacts first. "Of course we would," she scoffed, "what kind of parents do you think we are?"

Not reassured in the least, the height of my terror came later that week when I was going to the doctor for an unrelated issue (can anxiety-induced heartburn be considered unrelated?) and I asked him if there was any way I could have gotten rabies from another person, provided that they were rabid when we, uh, that is to say, you know, fit our pieces together.

He clutched his clipboard to his chest and discreetly eyed the distance to the door. "Uh, no," he said, edging slightly away from where I sat, clutching the paper on the exam table in both fists, "That isn't possible." Yeah right! What did he know? What was he, a doctor (yes)? My anxious brain immediately screened out this kind man's medically sound opinion, which is why, on the way out of the hospital, I stopped the next person with a stethoscope that made eye contact with me and literally asked the exact same question.

"Uhh, no," Second Doctor began, imperceptibly flattening herself against the wall as her scrubs subtly changed color to blend into the cinderblock, "No, there is no way... no way that could happen."

I can only imagine what I looked like, with my undereye bags and computer printouts and eyes full of panic. Because what I was really asking those poor medical professionals wasn't, "Can I get rabies from another person?" because duh, obviously you can only get it from another human through organ transplants (thanks Internet! I owe you one!). What I was asking was more like, Am I going to be all right even if I have no idea what I am doing at any point (i.e., when having sex with people who are not myself), and how are things going to turn out if I am making these terrifying decisions about how my brain and my body have relationships to other brains and the occasional boner, and what about this huge, new mystery of sex, in the huge, frightening mystery of my new city? How can I be sure that I won't get a disease that will rot my brain or a man who will rot my heart when I made them both vulnerable to the elements?

That night with him was baffling; one minute I was tentatively clutching at the hair on the back of his head, the whites of my eyes like saucers, anxiously glancing around in the room in the dark like a crazed muskrat, as this man took his good ol' time between my legs, pretty sure—no, positive—that I saw him refuse a glass of water at the bar. The next I was guffawing and kicking my legs in a Three Stooges–circle going, "Woo woo woo" and clutching him to me and sweat-sealing myself to his body like we were a package of cocktail weenies. My brain rolled over and over on itself trying to handle the two competing yowls: brain-stem lust and frontal-lobe caution. One was made of the worried promises I made myself once I realized that my adult body was mine to take care of, the other roused from its burrow by the feeling of stubble scraping against my neck. Despite my internal turmoil, I couldn't allow my heebie-jeebies to blow my access to the adorable mind and precious body of this boy, or eventually, other boys, other kitchens, other years, older me, a better understanding of infectious disease transmission. Over time both voices quieted down to an occasional comment under their breath, still antagonistic, though there is a part of me that would still prefer a vaccination history over peonies. You can never be too sure.

Sex Tape Thing

Matthew Lawrence

DAVE SUGGESTED MAKING A VIDEO, and I said okay. I had only met him about five minutes previously, but I couldn't think of a reason to say no. I don't really get off on exhibitionism per se, but I figured if that was his thing then who was I to complain? Dave pulled a waiting camcorder out from the dresser and pointed it toward the bed. He had done this before, clearly, but still I couldn't think of any reason to object.

Dave was a lot smaller than me, older and kind of academic looking, but in an alcoholic and scraggly way. His skin was baggy, like it wanted nothing to do with his bones, and I could see why. Plus there was something about him that made it seem like he had been teleported from 1971. Maybe it was his yellowy hair, or maybe it was just the house, a large split-level beachfront thing with severely sloped ceilings where every room had steps going either up or down. From what I could tell it was expensive, but also hadn't been redecorated or cleaned in about thirty years.

Once the camera was rolling, Dave took out a towel that was embroidered with the name of a porn company. He instructed me to sit on the towel at the edge of the bed, and then he gave me a blowjob that was completely unmemorable in every way. Except that Dave talked a lot, and actually there was just one thing that he kept repeating over and over. "Oh," he'd say. "The sexual pleasure. The sexual pleasure." It's hard not to laugh at someone who says this while in the throes of ecstasy. He wanted to snuggle, even though he was just skin and bones and more skin, and eventually I put my tongue down his throat. Normally I reserve the kissy stuff for people I actually like, but it was the only way I could think of to shut him up.

After Dave came, which thankfully didn't take very long, he handed me the money and asked if I was listed on any escort websites. When I told him that I was new to the field and only used Craigslist, he quickly named about ten or twelve different sites and told me the pros and cons of each of them. He also told me that I should consider quitting my day job, because I was a nice alternative to all the muscle jocks and hairless twinks he usually saw. Dave said he liked that I never worked out and didn't shave or trim. And then he told me about his friend.

"I have a friend," Dave said. "He lives in Maine and he's married, but I've been seeing him about twice a month for about ten years now. I'd like the two of you to meet. Maybe you could even do a video together. He's a total top. Do you ever bottom?"

Like I said, I was new to the profession. Actually, Dave was only my third or fourth client ever. It was winter, and I didn't have any heat in my apartment, so my roommate had politely suggested that I start selling sex since I spent so much time of my time sleeping with unattractive old people, anyway.

I told Dave I'd think about meeting his friend, and he sent me home with a videotape so I could make a more informed decision. It took him about ten minutes to find the right one, because the tall bureau in his bedroom was completely filled with videocassettes packed two deep.

As I drove home, I thought about listing myself on some of the websites that Dave told me about, but the trouble was that I lacked three things that are vitally important if you want to be an Internet-based rentboy. First of all, I didn't have the Internet. I posted the Craigslist ad from my friend's house and checked for emails from prospective clients at the library. So that was a problem.

A bigger problem is that I didn't have a cell phone. I thought they were cumbersome and cancer-causing and I didn't trust myself to sign up for an expensive plan, because I knew I'd probably just lose the phone or drop it in the toilet or something. I could call clients from my landline, but I couldn't call for directions if I was lost, or call for help if something bad happened.

The biggest problem is that I didn't have a car. Outcalls would be easier, I thought, since I wouldn't have to pretend I had heat in my apartment, but anything outside the city was a total pain. Most of my friends didn't have cars, and the ones that did all drove sticks, which I don't know how to drive. Renting a car was out of the question, because I wasn't yet twenty-five and already had bad credit, anyway.

When I got home, I popped in the video Dave gave me. Suddenly all of my logistical concerns vanished, because Dave's friend was maybe the hottest man I had ever seen. He was kind of a muscle bear, but in that New England-y way where you could tell he got all his muscles by chopping wood or something. He was hairy and balding a little and he had a handsome face and his ass was perfect and his penis was roughly the size and firmness of a Santeria candle. I got so excited about meeting this man that I immediately jerked off, even though this video unfortunately also featured Dave, who was even less attractive on camera than in person, and who wouldn't stop moaning about the sexual pleasure.

It wasn't until after I finished jerking off that I realized something was amiss. I couldn't place it right away, but suddenly it hit me, and I became very, very confused. See, the video of Dave and his friend included a lot of cuts and a lot of different angles. In fact, after a minute or two I realized that there were at least four different cameras in the room that day, and two of them, from what I could tell, must have been in the bedroom's slanty ceiling.

For some reason this didn't freak me out so much as just confuse me. I wondered whether my video with Dave was also actually shot from multiple angles. I wanted to meet him again, partly to see where the cameras were and partly to get a copy of that tape.

Now, as I mentioned, I didn't have a car at the time. So when Dave emailed asking me to go back, I couldn't actually get there right away. He tried to tempt me with fifty dollars more than I had asked the first time. And then a hundred dollars more.

And then two hundred dollars more. And when Dave offered me three times what he paid the first time, I knew I had to do something.

So I called Leo. Leo was my roommate's unemployed boyfriend. He smoked pot all day and listened to a lot of Viking metal. He also lived in a dark and damp warehouse that was used as a facility to store vegetables. Leo wanted something to do and offered to be my driver, so I called Dave and set up a date for later in the week.

Now, the thing about the vegetable storage facility is that you could only hear the doorbell in the front room, which is where Leo usually spent his days getting stoned and playing video games. The thing about me is that I didn't have a cell phone to call Leo if he was somewhere besides the front room when I got there. And the thing about Leo is that the night before I was supposed to meet Dave, he drank three quarters of a bottle of Jägermeister.

It all worked out okay. Totally coincidentally, someone I knew rode by on her bike and let me use her phone. I couldn't remember anybody's number, but I called information and they gave me my roommate's work number and then I called my roommate at work and she called Leo and then Leo woke up and came outside and got me. We were behind schedule, but we could still make it, and everything was A-OK.

Sort of.

Leo was a little bit of a mess that day. Driving to Dave's we had to pull off the highway twice for puke breaks. Once we got into the small but affluent Boston suburb Dave lived in, Leo puked out the window every time we got to a stop sign. We couldn't find the street at first, so there were a lot of stop signs.

We made it, but I was late and freaking out a little. I felt sorry for making Leo drive when he was so pukey, and I felt sorry that I didn't have a phone to tell Dave I was running late. When I arrived, Dave could tell I was a little discombobulated, although he didn't actually seem bothered by my tardiness. He invited me in and offered me a soda and asked me to take my pants off. Everything was fine.

Now, the funny thing about Dave is that I couldn't figure out who he was or what he did. I knew Dave wasn't his real name, because I had Googled his full name and learned that Dave was the name of Frank Sinatra's character in a popular movie from 1958. But I could see from Dave's kitchen that maybe he did a lot of entertaining. His small fridge was stocked like a hotel room minibar, with tiny cans and bottles of every conceivable soft drink. I opted for a ginger ale, and it wasn't until Dave bent over to get it that I saw the TV.

There was a small black-and-white monitor sitting on the kitchen table, And on that monitor I could see the road leading up to Dave's driveway. And in that driveway I could see Leo's car. I could also see Leo, standing next to his car, puking out what few guts he had remaining.

It suddenly seemed vitally important that I had to get Dave out of the kitchen, and the only way I could think of to do that was to feign extreme horniness. If he saw the little Viking metal guy puking in his driveway, he might ask me to leave, and the whole pukey trip would have been for nothing.

It worked, I thought, because soon enough we were in the bedroom, and Dave was getting the camcorder out again. He had me lay on the porn towel again, but this time he wanted to give me a rimjob. This was great, because with my legs in the air I had a chance to study the bedroom ceiling.

And I couldn't find anything. Strange.

The rimjob went on for the longest twenty minutes ever, with Dave pausing every once in a while to moan his trademark phrase about the sexual pleasure, but he got off pretty quickly again. Afterward, he told me that he had talked to his friend in Maine, but that the guy wasn't interested.

As I left that day with enough money to pay my rent and utilities for the month, I had a sinking feeling that Dave would never write to me again. And he didn't.

When I got home, I put on the video of Dave giving me the blowjob. It was bad. Really, really bad. The dresser and the bed were exactly the same height, so sixty percent of the screen was taken up by my enormous white thighs. Every once in a while you'd see my head pop up, like I was part of some weird Whac-A-Mole game. There were no other camera angles, and I had to shut the video off without getting to the end.

Bambino

Gina de Vries

I'D TOLD HIM TO DRESS LIKE A TEENAGER going on a first date, and he came over that night looking sharp—all James Dean tough and tender. Black curls coiffed into a greaser pompadour, leather jacket and dark jeans and pressed button-down shirt hugging his tall, slim frame. He'd just seen *East of Eden*, he said. "The hype is real—James Dean really is that hot. I'm kind of in love."

I grinned. "So that's why you're dressed like a greaser!"

He nodded. "Yeah. The movie's probably better when you're stoned, because it's a little slow. But it's awesome, and James Dean..." His eyes got all dreamy again.

"Do you wanna fuck him or do you wanna be him, Bambino?"

"Um. Both." He blushed.

•

He made me wish I had a record player, that boy. A record player and a claw-foot tub, real silk stockings and a rotary phone. A collection of vintage garter belts and a smart little sixties miniskirt that inched up my thighs slowly when I spread my legs. A dress for him to unzip down the back while I insisted that of course I wasn't doing anything untoward and really, I was getting tired of him insinuating something. He made me want a beret and a first edition of *Howl*, a couple of joints and a bottle of red wine to seduce him into the wicked bohemian lifestyle. He made me want an apron collection, a real kitchen, and a real dining room. A table where I could feed him after-school snacks and help him with his homework, undo his belt while he struggled with a Math problem and tried to ignore how good my hands felt.

What I had to work with was a tiny rent-controlled apartment, thrift store lingerie, and a limitless imagination. We started dating right before I started graduate school and moved into an impossibly cheap in-law studio in the South Mission. The day after our first date, he offered to help me move. He ended up stuck in transit on a trip back from Oregon—never made it to move-in. But five days later, he was the first person I fucked in my new bedroom.

I'd never lived alone before. This was a place with a fig tree in the backyard, an old-school San Francisco Chinese grandmother landlord who offered to let me pay rent in cash, and a sketchy little alleyway between buildings that led up to my doorstep. I wanted to throw him around in that alley, but there was zero privacy—no way to do it without alerting my new neighbors to the intimate details of my sex life. This was a place with a kitchenette table that doubled as a counter, and a main room that just barely held my bed, my bookshelves, my desk, and my clothes. But it didn't matter that it was tiny—it was mine, all mine. I could put whatever I wanted on the walls, have loud sex without disturbing my housemates, sing opera at three in the morning if the whim struck me. Everything about that month felt limitless, imbued with magic and newness—my new school, my new apartment, my new neighborhood, my new cat. And him.

And I didn't have an apron collection or a first edition of *Howl*, so I worked with what I did have. I started scouring thrift store racks, looking for the slips with 42-inch bustlines and lots of give in the tits. I grabbed every H&M size 12 camisole off the rack and stretched them over my curves. I bought $9 stay-up stockings at Madame S and $2 fishnets from MultiKulti Dance Accessories on 16th and Valencia. I justified every new purchase, no matter how extravagant or frivolous, with "Well, I can use it in a role-play, right? This slip is actually a very reasonably priced sex toy!" I started wearing more makeup. Dangly earrings instead of my tough-girl gauged lobes. Flowers in my hair. "Hellfire" from Black Phoenix Alchemy Lab dabbed into the sweet spots behind my ears and between my breasts.

I was only a year older than him, but when we went out together, we really did look the part. Me like Mrs. Robinson in my leopard-print skirt and garters and stockings. Him like Benjamin in his pressed pants and shirt, that dark mop of curls, big eyes and pale creamy skin. The adorable jolty way he moved when he was nervous, or excited—so much boy energy to burn. Dimples in his cheeks when he smiled. The tentative, tender, teenage way he'd ask permission to touch me, or lean into the crook of my neck and sigh, so happy.

I was wearing fishnets with stompy boots in the pit at Cypher in Snow shows by the time I was fourteen, calling myself queer and punk and femme even then. Pervert came a few years later, when I was still a teenager. When I met him, I'd been a die-hard Daddy's girl for years; I'd even been Ma'am and Mistress a few times. But I'd never been in charge all the time. I'd never been anyone's Mama before.

♠

"So much of this," he said to me, "Is about getting to have the adolescence I didn't get to have." We were stretched out in my bed, him in his greaser finery, me in my lingerie, catching up on our weeks before we got carried away by sex.

"I thought you might say something like that," I said. I still didn't know much about his life, then. But I know what it is to be raised to be a good girl, what it is to be expected to grow into a proper woman; and I know what it is to fail at that. I can't imagine what it's like to be held up to the Girl Standard when you're actually a boy waiting to grow into a man.

"You know... It's like that for me, too," I said, "When I play Mama with you, sometimes. And when we both pretend we're teenagers..."

And he looked surprised. "But weren't you, like, the cool punk girl who came out all early? Like, didn't you do zines and all this awesome writing and—?"

"Yeah, I mean, I was punk and I was queer, but I was a nerd and I was a fat girl, too. Publishing a zine didn't get me laid in high school, dude." And we both cracked up at that.

"It's funny," I said, "I mean, I think the kids I went to school with thought I was a slut because I was queer, so, you know, that automatically makes you hypersexual—"

"Right, of course, they always think that—"

"—and, I mean, I dressed the part, and I talked about sex. But I only had sex with one person in high school. I wanted to be slutty, but..." I trailed off. Tried to find the words. "It wasn't something I had access to. Some of what I do with you, when we pretend like that... It's about getting to be who I would have been if I'd actually been in my body. If I'd believed I was pretty. Believed I could be sexy like that."

♦

Sometimes I felt myself existing in the timeline of all the characters we played. Not just frozen at that age, but frozen in that time period. So when we pretended I was a bossy riot grrrl and he was the shy, younger grunge-rock boy who was friends with my dorky little brother, it wasn't 2009 in my studio. It was 1999 at my parents' house, and I was seventeen, playing him my Bikini Kill 7-inch and inching too close to him on my bed. I knew better than to be fooling around with my kid brother's friend—it was kinda questionable around the age thing, it was even more questionable when it came to the crowds we hung out in. But it was so much fun to make him squirm and swear him to secrecy, and God, he was such a quick study with that mouth, those hands, that cock.

The night he came over dressed up like a greaser I was in a red slip, fishnets, red heels. A glittery red cloth rose in my hair. Could I be a fifties housewife in this? I thought as we chatted. He was telling me more about James Dean. Maybe. A very seductive one, at least. We were lying on my bed together, close but not cuddling. I caught his chin in my hand and pulled him in for a kiss. He wrapped his arms around me, but he pulled his lips away after a minute.

"We're doing that thing we do," he murmured into my neck, kissed it. "Mmm.

We're doing that thing, where we start before the scene starts..."

"Oh, so you wanna work for it?" I grabbed his pompadour and pulled. He winced at first, cried out. But then he giggled. Nodded.

"I wanna work for it. Yes. I want a story."

I let him go. It was hard not to touch him.

"Okay, Bambino... How old do you wanna be?"

"Sixteen? Seventeen, maybe?"

"Okay, I think... I'm a housewife. You're my son's friend..."

"I've had a crush on you for a long time, yeah."

"And you've come over... And my husband happens to be on a business trip. And my son's out with those hoods he runs with." I felt my voice start to change, subtly. It got lower. More serious. "Why are you over here, kid? Shouldn't you be out with those boys, too? Not that I approve..."

His eyes got big. He had never looked more earnest to me. "No, I'm good, Ma'am. I don't hang out with those boys. I don't like that your son hangs out with them." Then he cracked a smile. Started laughing. "Wait, wait—I'm sorry, I just thought of something. Can I be fucking your son, too?!"

That got me laughing. "Pervert!"

"No, no, hear me out. So you want me, but you're angry with me, because I'm taking your son away from you. You want me, but you think I'm a bad influence."

"You're a glutton for punishment, little faggot." I grabbed a curl and pulled again.

He shrieked, but he looked like the cat with the canary in his mouth. "Guilty as charged."

♠

I listened to *Diamond Dogs* over and over again the summer we got together. If I'd had the record player, I would have worn out the vinyl, I'm sure. Music takes on a different meaning when you're falling for someone, and I was falling, hard—for him, but for my new self, too. The whole relationship was a coming out moment, coming out into something different and new, and like most people who are newly out and overzealous, I ran into it full-tilt, no holds barred, not a single stop or hesitation. No checking to see if there were any obstacles. No worries that maybe I'd trip over that rock and skin my knee. I didn't think. I just ran. Everything was intense; everything felt like a whirlwind of emotions and sex. I still use words like pivotal and formative to describe our months together, and god, I fear I'm being grandiose, melodramatic talking that way. But that's what it was. It's how we were with each other.

So that month, falling for him, listening to *Diamond Dogs* because it happened to be what I'd picked up from the library on a whim—suddenly, I took the album very personally. It was the soundtrack to the crush, and it was the soundtrack to my newfound Mama persona. It felt like every line of every song was written especially for me. "Sweet Thing" was an anthem, Bowie's creepy-sexy snarl in my ear, the perfect music for dating this boy who was glam rock and choir boy, French new wave and faggotry, lisp and snarl, James Dean and Lou Reed, cocksure and shy violet. Dating this boy who wanted nothing more than to suck my cock, who wanted nothing more than to fuck me so good, just right. *When you rock'n'roll with me, there's nowhere else I'd rather be. We're taking it hard all the time. I love you in your fuck-me pumps, and your nimble dress that trails. Boys, boys, it's a sweet thing. Mmm, if you want it, boys? Get it here.*

♠

His hands on my tits were sweet, that night. Tentative. "Oh, honey. You're not so tough, are you? You're just a little pussycat under all that bravado, huh?" He made a little whimpering noise—the pink rose to his cheeks and his eyelashes fluttered. But he didn't take his hands away. Something about how soft and unsure he was made me want to up the ante.

"Nobody's touched me like this for a long, long time. Not my husband. Not my son." I heard him catch his breath at that. Good. "Nobody." I leaned in to kiss him. He was so pliant in my arms, a rag doll of a boy, a marionette, but god, the noises he made. Little moans and sighs, and he licked the crook of my neck and whispered. "Oh, your skin tastes so sweet, Ma'am. I like it."

I pushed him back on the bed. He kept looking up at me in wide-eyed wonder. Or was it fear? Uncertainty? His breathing was heavy, and he was moaning, though. He'd tell me if he was real-life scared, right? I pulled his leather jacket off. Leaned down between his legs and started to unbuckle his belt. "Have you done this before, baby?"

"In a way," he said. Smirking.

"In a way?"

"I can't talk about it." And suddenly, the smirk melted from his face, and he looked so little. "Ma'am... There's a woman I do this with in my dreams."

"In dreams?" I hated that I was repeating everything he said. But I wasn't expecting that from a greaser boy. In dreams? What do I say to that? "Do you touch yourself in these dreams?"

He shuddered. "Sometimes, Ma'am."

So I put my hand on his zipper and stroked. "Show me how you like to do it."

He reached down and started to unzip. But then he froze. Turned over on his side, and curled up into a fetal position. "I need to stop—I'm sorry." I'd never seen him cry before. I was dumbfounded. What had I done? Was this about gender? Sexual assault? Shame? Maybe even just not being horny any more? Swallow your ego, I said to myself, He needs you right now.

"Baby. It's okay. No apologies."

"I—" He blinked. He looked so surprised. "The character's too repressed and fucked up. I'm getting too into it. I feel real-life ashamed."

"No worries, Bambino." I pulled him into my arms. "You're so sweet. Honey, you're so good." But what I most wanted, in that moment, was to be told those things myself.

•

I started calling him Bambino after I saw *Murmur of the Heart* for the first time. It's the Louis Malle film about the adventures of a precocious—sexually, intellectually, otherwise—fourteen-year-old boy named Laurent. It's most famous for its frank but somehow uncreepy depiction of incest. The boy has sex with his mother at the end, consensually. He said the boy in the movie was a big influence on him, made an impression when he was first coming into s/m and wanted to cultivate a boy persona. So I felt like I was learning as much about him as I was about the movie when I watched it over salad and pizza one night after class.

"I'm making this movie out to be supererotic," he'd said, "But it's probably not that sexy. I think I just get off on the cocky rich French boy thing." From the first moment, the opening wail of Charlie Parker, where towheaded Laurent and his friend are out on the cobblestoned French streets scamming tourists out of their pocket change by pretending to collect for the Red Cross, I was just riveted. I could not take my eyes off the screen. The boy is called Laurent by his French family, but Venzino by his Italian mother, a gorgeous, doe-eyed woman from a meager background. I read her as a sex worker, even though I'm not sure if that's what Malle intends. She's not whoring in the film, but you get the distinct sense that she married the boy's father for money. That they met under less than proper circumstances. It's a story full of sex and jazz and the intense push/pull between love and resentment. Venzino has a lot of homoerotic encounters with his brothers—not quite sex, and not quite sexy, so they are somehow less shocking than when he and his mother touch each other, but it is still surprising. The sex scene with his mother at the end is so bizarrely normal that you almost forget that it's an incest scene. Except that that's also what gives it a charge, a spark—that they are fundamentally not supposed to desire each other this way, mother and son, teenage boy and middle-aged woman, but they do.

In the movie, Laurent's mother calls him "Venzino" as a pet name, a kind of sweet Italian diminutive of his French name. And it occurred to me that my boy should have a pet name, and for some reason, it was "Bambino." It just was. It's Italian for "baby boy," which seemed perfect. Growing up, it was the nickname I heard my Calabrese grandmother and great-aunts bestow upon all my boy cousins. It also refers to manifestations of the Baby Jesus, which was less perfect. But I liked it, and I started calling him that, casually. "Bambino, how are you?" "Bambino, fetch that for me."

It took him a while to ask me what it meant. I'd been calling him Bambino for a couple weeks, and he finally said "Whoa! I just looked up this thing you're calling me. Are you calling me the little baby Jesus?!!!" This was over an instant message conversation. He put three exclamation points at the end of the sentence, he was that taken aback. "No, no. Sweetie, it's Italian for 'little boy.' I'm calling you a little boy." And he sent me back a smileyface.

♦

He started to change, curled up in my arms. I could feel the desire returning to him—whatever demon he'd wrestled with was floating away. "I want to keep going," he said, "Maybe we could do something lighter? Just jerk off together? But be the same characters?"

"Of course, honey."

"No, or maybe. I mean." He was talking fast, now, I could see the wheels in his head spinning. "I mean, do you want me to fuck you?"

"I... I mean, if you want to, I'd love that."

"Okay. Maybe we can do that, as long as you're running it, showing me how." He smiled big. “I really want to, Mama.”

“Mmm.” I kissed his eyelids. “You want to touch me?”

He kissed my neck. “Yes.”

“You want to show me how you touch yourself?” And the minute I said it, I regretted it. Fuck. That’s what hurt him before. How could I be so dumb?

But he was reaching for his fly again, saying “Yes.” He got his jeans down over his hips and ass. Then he crumpled.

“Fuck. I’m sorry. I need to stop.”

“I’m sorry. God, I’m so sorry. I fucked up. Shit.”

So we held each other for the rest of the night. Read each other stories. Ate ice cream. Went to sleep curled up in each other’s arms.

•

We woke up that morning curled around each other like kittens. I started stroking his hair, absentminded, half-asleep; he stroked my face, and suddenly, everything felt electric again. My hands were all over him in a flash. He rolled over onto his belly, grinding his hips into my sheets and sighing as I raked my nails over his back. “I—you really wanna do this?” I was still gun-shy from the night before. I couldn’t believe I was back-pedaling out of sex with someone I was so hot for, but I wanted to make sure. “Honestly, I didn’t intend to be Evil Molesting Mommy and fuck you awake...”

“No, it’s my favorite way to wake up. Please don’t stop.”

I didn’t need to be told twice. “Do you want me in the back or the front hole?”

“The front, please.”

"Do you want my hands or my cock?"

"Your cock, *please.*" That edge in his voice, so full of desire it was hoarse, guttural.

I slipped into my strap-on so fast I fumbled with it. I fumbled when I fucked him, too—I'm short, and he was tall, and balancing on my knees behind him on the bed was hard. After I slipped out the third time, I couldn't help it, I started giggling.

"What's funny?" He moaned.

"My dick keeps slipping out of you from this angle. Can you turn over, pretty? Or can we bend you over the bed?"

"No, I wanna be on my belly."

"Then I need to use my hands."

"Anything, just don't stop, please Mama."

He came fast around my fingers, snarling and pounding the mattress while I told him how good he was, how hot he was, how much I loved fucking him. I pulled out, pulled the glove off, pulled him close to me. I was so wet; I wanted him to touch me so bad. I leaned in to kiss him, and he stilled. He looked close to crying again.

"I'm sorry. I'm not doing well. I'm sorry. It's just hard sometimes, getting fucked fucks with my sense of myself, and I feel like less of a boy, and I'm sorry, I want to touch you, but..."

So I held him while he broke again. Fought to urge to say I love you. "Baby. It's okay."

•

Sometimes I felt guilty, needy for wanting that affection. *He says we're just casual. Do I get to want that? He's a big kid, I can ask and he can say no, but what if even asking is too much? Is that pressure? Pushing?* I'd daydream, and then I'd feel greedy for being daydreamy. I'd want little presents from him, the kind of gifts you buy for someone because you see or hear something and it makes you think of them—a notebook with a pretty cover, a small stuffed snail with pink antennae, a mix CD. Sometimes I wanted big presents, too—a new knife, tickets to see Patti Smith when she came into town that October. Sometimes I wanted the Lloyd Dobler moment—him standing outside my window in the rain, boombox above his head, grinning about me.

And sometimes, I just wanted him near me. I wanted him to come over with popcorn and a movie at 9 o'clock on a Sunday night when I'd had a terrible week. But I didn't ask. I didn't ask, because he'd said he needed to cool down and he could only see me once a month and we had to be more casual, because he was overwhelmed, but he'd still text and email me all the time, we'd have phone dates, he'd say, over and over, how honored, privileged, amazed he was to be in my life. Where was I in his life, though? He called himself my friend as well as my lover, but he wasn't the kind of friend I could rely on when I was having a bad day. He wasn't the kind of friend I could call and ask to come over the awful day I ran into my rapist at a poetry reading, I came home to a letter that said I didn't get the big grant I applied for, and then my septic system exploded when I tried to take a hot shower. My close friends could do that for me—my best friend, with a girlfriend and friends and a busy life, she made time to come over that night with ice cream and hugs and an offer to take a bubble bath in her tub. Why couldn't someone I was ostensibly dating do that, too?

♠

We both took showers. Studied at a café together, split a piece of ginger-pear bread while I tried to write a response paper for my evening class, and he worked on his zine. We took a walk to the Mission Library after. I was so pent up, with sadness and lust and this feeling of missing him even though he was right in front of me. "I..." I finally said, "I... still feel really sexual." Why did it feel so naked, saying what I wanted? I got to want things, right? "I have go home to Oakland," he said. He looked embarrassed. For himself or for me?

At the library, I borrowed a random DVD of *Arrested Development*, and he borrowed another Louis Malle movie. We hugged awkwardly at the BART train. My apartment is only a five-minute walk from BART; I was crying before I got through my front door. I collapsed into my bed, sobbing, and eventually reaching for my vibrator. I cried and jerked off and cried while I jerked off, thinking about all the things I wanted to do with him, all the places I wanted him to touch me that he hadn't. Thinking about every question that was left hanging on my tongue. *What did I do? Why did he go away? Am I too much? I just want a place in his life. I just want to matter.*

I went to my evening class, exhausted, rings around my eyes, questions still ringing in my head. Am I a monster? Do I want too much? What did I do wrong? I could barely focus in class, didn't hear a word anyone said. I couldn't wait to get home. I thought about calling him the minute I got in the door. I decided to send a text and watch *Arrested Development* instead. "bambino, i'm feeling a spot of top drop. can you reassure me i'm only evil in good ways?" Of course every minute he didn't respond made me feel worse than before. Maybe the text wasn't a good idea.

I put on my pink lights and my softest pajamas, put the DVD on my laptop, and settled back into a cocoon of blankets. I just wanted something silly to take my mind off my day, something to watch while I collapsed. The first episode on the DVD was called "Motherboy XXX"—about a mother/son bonding dance. I laughed, hard, for the first time all day, but it was the kind of laughter that verged on tears. I didn't wanna start crying again. I pulled my blankets even tighter around myself as the credits rolled. My cat took pity on me. She let me press my face into her fur like she was a pillow, curled up around my head, she purred even louder and licked my face. Everything I could do to feel held that night, I did.

Work

Stephen Elliott

I WAS KIND OF TRYING SOMETHING. She was lying in her bed, and I was lying behind her in her underwear. They were a swamp green with light green lace along the top. I was surprised they fit me. She had a "no pants in her bed" rule. At first, when I moved my hand across her stomach, she pushed my hand away. But the second time she let me and I slipped my thumb into her waistband and got my finger inside her before she could protest. Soon I had her panties around her knees and then her ankles and then just one ankle. This is basically a true story.

She was the kind of person that looked like she had long legs but didn't. We had half an hour left. For the previous three and a half hours she had been telling me she didn't want to have a sexual relationship with me. She said it was "a bad idea." She didn't know why it was a bad idea, it was just a feeling she had. We had gone for ice cream, then walked through the cemetery near her house. I wanted to stop under a tree or sit on a bench, but she wanted to keep moving. She said we should just be friends. But we weren't friends, and I had gotten wise to what she was doing, because she did it every time. It was rejection as foreplay. So now, when I saw her, I knew I would eventually get inside.

She had a small vagina and would only let me use one finger. I would kneel in front of her as if searching for something, my index finger drumming her bladder and my tongue pressing her clit. She would lay motionless and make little noises and occasionally say "Oh God." It wasn't an exclamation, it was a tiny thing escaping from her. I wanted her to sit on me. I wanted to suffocate under her. But I knew that wouldn't happen. It would be too much work for her to get on top of me, and she was lazy.

She had a boyfriend, but they were taking a break. He had a good job, and he was Asian, like her. She didn't think Asian women should date white guys. Part of their break included her promising she wouldn't have sex with me. I didn't think that was fair. We had started having sex while they were still dating but only when someone was taking pictures. She would post the pictures to her website claiming it wasn't cheating; it was work.

I was in love with her. I knew she would go back to her boyfriend soon.

"You only like me because I reject you," she said.

"Maybe we should test it and find out. You could try not rejecting me for six months."

"I think I like you because you're funny," she said.

I went down on her for the whole thirty minutes. I loved the way she tasted, and I loved the way her thighs felt on my cheek. I think when you're in love you like things you wouldn't normally like, and people smell different. That's the only definition of love I know.

But maybe that's not love at all. Maybe that's just a drug addict's description of love. Because all of our interactions were a prolonged game. There was a goal, I wanted her naked, so I performed and performed until finally, satisfied, she laid back, closed her eyes, spread her legs, and let me take what I wanted. It was like payment for a service, for all that effort I put into making sure she wasn't bored. I was like a human television.

But if we ever really spoke about things, things that weren't just a veil for my ulterior motives, I wouldn't have known what to say. I don't think she would, either.

I would have liked to stay, with my face in her vagina, fallen asleep and woken up there, but we were out of time. I gathered my things and got dressed. There were handmade clay figures on the shelves, sheets of plastic filled with family pictures hanging on the walls, but not much else. From the window I could see a stand of trees and the driveway to a parking lot.

She said I could keep her panties.

"When will I see you again?" I said.

"I don't know," she said. "I don't like making plans."

Later, I would say I missed her, and she wouldn't respond. She took her boyfriend back. I did my best to hover, to wait in the wings, but there weren't any crumbs. I had a feeling she was the last woman who would ever smell like that, because nobody smells like that. I had a feeling I had pushed my luck too many times, always leaving my money on the table, always picking door number 4. I could say the moments of ecstasy were worth it. Any story can be a happy story if the author wants it to be. It's just a matter of choosing your ending.

I loved her, but I didn't like her. I thought I should work on that, but I was tired of working on things. What I'm saying is when you're one age you go to the beach and you see the sun set and it's like the ocean's been lit on fire, and when you're another age you go to the beach and you see the same thing and you think, "I should do this more often." What I'm saying is I had already turned my life around many times, charted new paths. She was a sex worker, and one day I just offered to pay her. But by the time I thought of asking she had already quit doing that. She said it wouldn't be fair to take my money when she no longer felt like doing sex work; her heart wouldn't be in it. She was considering going back to school, looking to do something else.

I'll Be The One To Break My Heart

Arielle Brousse

I WAS DOING THE MATH IN MY HEAD as I rounded the corner to his street. Sixteen, I concluded, as I rang the buzzer to his apartment. He was sixteen years older than me.

I was the only person on the sidewalk, and I wondered how I looked, shifting my weight from foot to foot in front of the door, which was isolated on the side of the building, flush with a flat, beige stucco wall. It hardly looked like a welcoming place. It was a weird, piecrust scrap of an apartment, from those Philadelphia neighborhoods where they've haphazardly chopped old houses into segmented living spaces without much thought to symmetry. The front door was his, but it opened only wide enough to allow you to sidestep onto a long staircase to his tiny second-floor living room. I took a deep breath and used the time it took him to descend to compose myself, pulling at my clothes. I ran my fingers through my hair and rubbed my thumbs at the corners of my mouth to make sure my lipstick was all in place. I wanted to look good. I wanted to remind him why he invited me.

It worked; the red door swung open, and he was there. He met my gaze then left it to give me a once-over. He grinned.

"Come in," he said, and I leaned in for a kiss on the cheek.

I passed him and starting climbing the stairs before he'd had a chance to lock the door behind us. My hips were swaying by the time he turned his head.

Sixteen isn't much more than twelve, I thought, as I mounted the stairs.

Twelve was the number of years between me and the fiancé I'd broken up with a handful of months ago. My engagement had lasted only two years, which was about how long the man coming up the stairs behind me had been married to the woman who was technically still his wife. They'd been separated for about as many months as I'd been single—hence the out-of-the-way apartment—and the divorce would be final by the next week. It was only, he assured me, a matter of paperwork.

I'd met him when I was eighteen. He was a writer who worked in the same city I'd just moved to. He took a special interest in me and my writing when no one else did, and I had all the complicated feelings you might expect from a teenage girl who wants to believe someone sees something special in her.

Just after I'd ended things with my fiancé and the writer had separated from his wife, we had run into each other on the sidewalk. He put the kickstand up on his bike to ask "how it'd been going" with me, and I restricted my answers to statements about my new job. I had heard about the end of his marriage, but I kept my questions to the publication of his new book. It was he who softened his voice first, sharpening his gaze, "I heard about you and him."

He offered his sympathies and when I accepted, explaining, it's all for the best really, he told me he'd known. Told me he always knew it wasn't going to work between us, that he always thought my fiancé and I had just been at different places in our lives. Then he offered up his own ending to tie onto mine. "You might have heard that I'm separated now. We tried to make it work, therapy and all that." He sighed and paused, a deliberate, almost dramatic pause. "But I guess it just wasn't meant to be." We did the mutual consolation thing that any acquaintances might, but I knew what was coming from the way he held eye contact longer than was merely polite, the way that after he hugged me good-bye he said he thought I was great, and that I was going to do so much better. He hadn't told me about his separation as part of a friendly interchange. This had been a suggestion.

I'd been looking for suggestions.

When, weeks later, we'd run into each other at a bar for a mutual friend's party—and when, emboldened by the noise and the alcohol, he'd gently pulled me by the wrist into him from behind, hotly whispering into my ear, "Come home with me tonight"—I did, briefly. We shared a drink and a few side glances shot with perfect aim, and then announced I was going home, knowing that the next time I chose to come back, I'd fuck him.

I imagined myself graceful and lithe and seductive. I imagined my body white and glowing in his beige-gray apartment. I imagined myself being everything he'd been missing in his sad marriage and I imagined becoming everything I'd been missing in myself. I imagined using his age and experience to propel me out of my college years, into my young adulthood. I imagined myself drinking from him. I imagined eating him alive.

♦

In his living room, I noticed he'd set out a small dish of nuts on his coffee table. As if that was something bachelors ever did, as if he'd forgotten he wasn't hosting a mixer.

I gave him my coat as he was telling me, "Thanks for coming," too formally for what I'd imagined.

"It's my pleasure," I said. "I'm sorry I'm late."

"I'm just happy you're here," he told me. "Can I get you a drink?"

And thank god he offered. I watched him as he opened a bottle of Rioja, and remembered the impetus for my schoolgirl crush. He had neatly cropped black hair and kind, ice-blue eyes; his eyebrows weren't bushy, but they were thick and serious and furrowed when he thought. His cheeks were less rugged, rosy even, almost boyish. He was just taller than me (I thanked myself for wearing flats), but his shoulders were broad, and his forearms were strong; I watched them brace themselves as he poured, and relax in turn when he brought me my glass and joined me on the couch. "Thank you," I murmured.

We talked about his book and the classes he was teaching for quite a while, interspersed with the only vaguely relevant stories from your youth that always seem to make their way into a conversation driven by wine and getting-to-know-you. I'd kicked off my shoes by this point and tucked my legs up behind me, leaning an elbow on the back of the couch. Laughing came more easily after a while. We each had a glass of wine or three, which gave us little opportunities to touch, to flirt—him guiding my hand on the stem of the glass to even things out when he'd poured too much for himself.

I listened to him, letting his words float around me while I took in the scene. I liked the intensity of the color in his eyes and the way the creases at their corners showed just a little bit of his age.

I went to set down my empty glass and had trouble finding a clear spot on the book-strewn coffee table.

"I apologize for the mess," he chuckled, when he noticed. He bent over and stacked some of them neatly, making space for me.

"You know, usually this shit's just thrown wherever. It's a little embarrassing once I know someone's looking at it."

"Oh, not at all," I laughed back, running my hand through my hair. "It just looks like you're hard at work. Is this a new book, or—?"

"Yeah, actually. I—have you ever been to Chris'?"

"Chris who?"

"Oh, it's—no, it's a jazz club where a bunch of my old buddies hang out, and we jam sometimes. Anyway this new book has been a little bit bent toward the music and—"

"Wait, jam? What do you play?"

"Ah, yeah, trumpet, you didn't know?"

"Why would I know?"

"Heh. Right. No, I was—before this—," he said gesturing to his notebooks, "I was a musician. Majored in music in college and all that. I was serious. And I was fucking good, actually."

"Wow," I said. "So what changed?"

He smiled at me, slowly. "Met the right people, I guess."

"Aha," I said, and took a deliberate sip from my wineglass, which had somehow been refilled. He watched me.

"Oh, speaking of..." he trailed off as he jumped off the couch and toward the stereo. "Speaking of music, and the right people..." He treated his CDs a bit like he did his books; there were stacks of them, some out of their cases, flung into corners of his built-in bookshelves. After he sorted through the stacks for a bit, he put one on. It was Feist's "I Feel it All."

"Oh hey," I grinned. "I just saw her at the Tower not long ago."

"Yeah?" He sighed and rejoined me on the couch. "This song—ugh. After we decided to separate, and before this, I was, uh, well, I was lost, you know? But there was a day where I was driving home from a reading in, like, the middle of nowhere, and this song came on, and I just—I just drove. I just drove, and there was this song, and everything was okay."

I smiled, knowing the feeling, and listened as the lyrics wound their way between us: "Ooh, I'll be the one to break my heart."

"I know what you mean," I said, shifting in my seat. "I mean—in finding something that seems like it gives meaning to what you're feeling. And a song can do that, even a fucking pop song, especially after a breakup, you know? I mean—you stake your future on this situation and you don't imagine it ever not being there, and then it's not and it's just like the bottom drops out. Even if it's not a painful breakup! Even if there's no animosity, there's just so much confusion there when your life changes that much, and the right song can be something you can hold on to. A defense against that, like, extravagant groundlessness you feel."

He gave me a flicker of what I thought was recognition, but then he put a finger to my lips and grabbed a scrap of paper on his table, leaning over to my side of the table to get to it. He was murmuring to himself almost breathlessly: "extravagant groundlessness." He wrote the words down in pencil in front of me. "Extravagant groundlessness. I've got to turn that into a poem."

Silent, I sipped my wine and overlooked it and smiled too much, unable to tell who was humoring whom.

He looked back up from his paper and held my gaze, then finally leaned in and kissed me. His mouth was smaller than I was used to. I kissed back with all the strategy I knew but couldn't push out of my mind how curious it was that something as silly as a kiss does have real variable qualities, that there was such thing as two people kissing who fit together, and this wasn't it.

He kissed me deeper. His hands landed on my thighs and hips, the side and back of my neck—thick, blunt hands that were unapologetic and indelicate. Now we were getting somewhere, I thought. I ran my fingers through his dark hair, light at first, tugging a bit in response to his aggression. He was leaning in harder, pressing me back a bit; I started to feel the real weight of him. I was almost certain he was just going to push me down on the couch and fuck me right there. Or so I hoped.

Instead of moving closer to me, for some reason he stood up and propelled himself to sit on the back of the couch, perched behind me with his legs on either side of my body. I had to twist around to look at him staring down at me. Too stunned to ask him what he was doing, I turned around to see. Before

I could object or question him, he leaned down and, in a lucky shot, gave me a bite on the exact spot on my throat that I like.

I surrendered, turning fully toward him, bringing myself up onto my knees on the couch cushions, reaching for his mouth, stretching myself to him. I let him grab, run his hands over me, my ass, my tits. I moaned and gasped just enough to let him know what I liked. I held on with my arms hooked around his shoulders, arched my back so my breasts thrust up toward his mouth, throwing my hair behind me, some of which must have caught his tongue as he licked up the nape of my neck.

I could have used this momentum to benefit from my positioning between his legs. I could have unzipped his jeans and teased him, gratified him on my own terms, taken back the power from beneath him. Before I could, though, he stopped his groping and just as quickly held my face in his hands, bringing his forehead down to touch mine, like we were in on some tender secret together.

"I'm so happy you're here, and I'm so incredibly turned on right now, if that isn't obvious." He gave a little laugh. "I think you're so cool," he said, and I half-smiled; "and you're so goddamn beautiful." I broke into the other half of the smile.

I was opening my mouth to say something back, something invitational, when he followed up with, "Yeah, you know you're beautiful."

I swallowed at the accusation.

He slipped back down onto the couch with me, his legs still around my body, ushering it into a snuggle position.

"Do you feel like guys your age appreciate you?"

The background sound felt like it cut out; I tried to decide whether I should leave, or how.

I couldn't tell you how we came to be in his kitchen, or why he was opening cabinets and drawers, rifling on shelves, but he must have realized that he was doing poorly and shifted gears. I'd told him when I'd first got there that I wasn't hungry. But there we were, off the couch, and he was flitting, manic and focused, bringing the candles he'd lit in the living room over onto the island where he was setting out paper-wrapped packages and tiny dishes. He ground pepper into a dish of olive oil and gushed, "This is the best fucking olive oil I've ever had. You have to try." I reminded him that I was allergic to the crackers he'd brought out for it, and he looked crestfallen for only a split second before asserting, "You need to just dip your finger in. Seriously." I told him that was ridiculous but a few sips of wine later he had me dunking the tip of my finger into the slick dish and sucking it off, relishing the earthiness that coated my palette.

This is all right, I thought. This was sensual, visceral, and he was good at it. If he'd just shut his mouth everything would work out.

He was already bringing something else out, working like a mad food scientist, and by the time I came to from the drowsy knockout of the olives he had his latest offering at the ready. His fingers grazed my lips as he fed me—"Try this," he said almost simultaneously to the act of entering my mouth, my complicity already implied. He'd rolled a walnut in maple syrup, and topped it with a tiny broken crumble of bleu cheese. He smiled to himself as my eyes rolled back into my head and I issued a little moan. He waited close until I swallowed, and then stepped even closer to kiss off the thin drizzle of syrup that remained on my lips.

We broke, still wet and sticky, and I sighed and smiled and let my hand fly to my mouth to cover it coyly, but he swept back in, took me by the wrists and pinned them above my head, against the wall. There he pressed me and kissed me again, hard, the length of his body on mine. It was all I could do to try to twist around him, embrace him with a raised thigh without the use of my arms. The tastes, the smell of the syrup still somewhere on someone's skin, the warm gold light, the exquisite pressure of his body and soft of his mouth, his tongue, and I felt like I was melting. Here he was being raw. Here he was using his body and his senses and little else. I forgave all. I remembered why I was here. I bucked my hips back into his, lifting my chin somewhat defiantly up to him. Telling him, in so many words, bring it on.

I could barely lift my eyelids when he bowed his head down, bringing his lips just a breath apart from mine, and murmured, "You're amazing."

And instead of blushing like I might have in a previous life, instead of looking down, then shyly back up through my eyelashes, I stared back hard. I twisted the corner of my mouth up and raised an eyebrow, letting him know I believed him. Let him be the one to blush, I thought. And with my eyes still fixed on his, boring into him, I led him to the bedroom.

There were clothes everywhere, piles of wool sweaters and crumpled button-downs that all seemed to be the same shade of blue, and he swept them all off the bed with an urgency I liked. I watched and idly played my fingertips where the hem of my sweater met my jeans, taking my time to make him hungry, curious to see which of them he would try to take off me first.

He practically tripped over the corner of his own bed in his attempt to get at my sweater as quickly as possible. He lifted it over my head and tossed it to a corner of the bedroom I didn't make note of, then brought his arms down immediately to the sides of my head to kiss me again, drawing his breath in through his nose strongly as he did so before fumbling to reach my bra clasp. It came off too, as did his sweater, and we were standing there with the satisfaction of skin-on-skin contact, my nipples hardening into his chest, the crotch of his pants hardening into mine.

I pressed him down on the bed first, and took a step back to slide off my jeans in front of him. I heard him utter a little sound, but couldn't classify it with vowels or consonants. Smirking still, I leaned over him to help his pants down.

I took particular pride in giving a good blowjob, the quality of the sighs and the moans I was able to elicit. I liked the twitches and the bucks and the skill it took to navigate them. I was ready to show off. When I made my grab for him I looked up to see what expressions were registering on his face, hoping for the boyish anticipation I so loved to see on a man. I stumbled a bit, mentally, when I looked and saw what I couldn't help but think was expectation rather than eagerness, like this was nothing worth noting, nothing any different from having allowed him to kiss my cheek upon entering the apartment. Well, I'll change his mind, I thought. I'll show him how outstanding this is.

I pulled out the works, working every muscle in my tongue. I tried to imagine the flush of my pink lips against my fair skin, how good that would look, but then I couldn't help wondering if he could even see me, whether his soft white belly, so much rounder than I'd thought, was blocking his view.

I did appreciate the sounds he made, the way he ran his fingers through my hair and gripped briefly in instances when I threw some new trick at him. This is worth it, I thought. Look what I can do. And when he pulled me up by the shoulder, signaling, I don't want to finish here, I thought, the hell you will, there's more to be done.

I rose to my knees and looked down on him, licking my lips, which were wet with the effort, waiting for him to rise to his knees so I could position myself to have him reciprocate. I imagined lying back on his pillows and gripping the sheets while I ground my pussy into his mouth, how my ribs would flex when I breathed hard, my body in such an arc.

Just as soon, however, as he had risen to his knees, he pushed me down and lifted my legs to his shoulders. At least he had an interesting angle in mind, I thought, so I went with it, certain I could work in the pussy eating a little later.

He shoved himself in with abandon, but the rush of pleasure I expected from his aggression never struck me. I tightened my knees into his shoulders, trying to grip him from within and intensify the feeling, but it was as if his body was working independently of mine. I needed to connect, but touching him with my hands was impossible since he was holding me down, so I whispered his name. He didn't answer or acknowledge; I thought perhaps he couldn't hear me over his grunts, so I called out to him again, trying to rise up into his body. He was thrusting and concentrating hard, looking down on his own pistoning cock, unaware of and seemingly uninterested in my efforts.

With my thighs pressed back to my chest, there wasn't much I could do to get his attention. So I closed my eyes and threw my head back on the pillow, exposing my throat, hoping for a kiss like the hungry ones he'd given me earlier. There was a pause, and I thought he was obliging, but instead he withdrew from me; I opened my eyes and sat up, looking at him and smiling and moving to him. He lunged forward, too, grabbing my sides with both arms. I wanted to push him down and straddle him, or else draw him down behind me into a spoon position with my leg lifted; but with his hands on my hips, in one strong, fell motion, he flipped me over onto my hands and knees. I twisted back to smile lustily at him—this was one of my favorite positions, even though the transition had been somewhat abrupt—but I never got the chance to see his face. Before my eyes met his, he put one hand down hard on my back, pressing my torso roughly to the bed, and brought my hips back up into his, with my lower back arched at an almost impossible angle. I bit my lip, ready to be taken hard, and he reared back and plunged in; but again, somehow, for all his forcefulness I felt almost nothing, or at least nothing I enjoyed. I felt separate from him, and I couldn't move to make the position work better for me. I tried to bring myself up on my hands, to buck and grind back into him, but his hand was so strong on my back I couldn't push myself up. I called out his name again, somewhat muffled by the comforter, and cried, "Oh god, deeper, please—!" But, immobilized and muted by him, I got no response.

We went through the motions of a few more positions, me always kept stiffly in place, him always deaf to my suggestions. I wanted to try; I wanted to feel something from him and give something back. I wanted to be open to the situation, but couldn't find a way. I wasn't his partner. I wasn't anything more than a line in his poem.

I'd spent more nights on my own in those past few months than I'd ever been used to enduring in a row, but beneath him, begging suggestions and changes and being roundly ignored, never considered as a sexual being myself in any capacity, I'd never felt quite so lonely.

When he finished, he was finished, and didn't ask me if I'd come. He took a deep breath and sighed it out, his wet breath rushing over my bare chest. He lifted his head and looked at me for the first time since before my clothes had come off, as if he'd suddenly noticed I was there in bed with him. He raised his eyebrows at me and smirked, giving out a one-syllable laugh as he pulled out and rolled off me. "Wow, huh?" he said, not really asking, grinning at the ceiling and rubbing his stomach. He brought a hand down on my naked thigh and let his head loll on his pillow to face me. "Still can't believe that happened!"

He looked back to the ceiling before I had a chance to answer him, so I didn't try. He brought his hand back up off me and ran it through his hair, which I now noticed was thinning slightly. He yawned like a lion and settled down into the covers with barely another word. I somewhat listlessly followed suit: turning away from him, staring at my bra on his bedroom floor, listening to the rhythmic sounds of his breathing fill the too-quiet room, trying desperately to lull myself to sleep.

The proportions of everything seemed off—his body, the room, the reactions—and I felt like I was in a strange and isolating dream. I spent the night. I'm not sure why I stayed, but I have the feeling that I needed daylight to sterilize the situation before I left it. Making my way home in the dark would have felt far too empty.

●

I turned down his invitation to brunch and walked myself back to West Philadelphia on a Saturday morning. I stopped just once at a farmers' market to buy and eat a single ripe fig, which was sweet but alien in texture, somewhere between flesh and cotton on my tongue. Three miles in absolute November sunshine seemed to make everything sharp. Even the sidewalk glared back.

At home I fed my cat and turned on the shower. I stripped absently while waiting for the hot water, taking glazed note of myself in the mirror: my curves, my pert breasts, the small patch of stretch marks on my lower belly where I had gained some weight and lost it. I was trying to make sense of what I saw, what I'd seen. What must I have looked like to him?

I washed and dried and stretched and laid in bed. I went out that night with another boy, and the next week with yet another, and so on for months before I found someone who seemed to make me forget what loneliness meant. In between, I enjoyed their company, and I enjoyed the way they fucked me, and I enjoyed, I noted, how one grew out of the other, and not the other way around.

The Death of J. G. Ballard

William Ball

By the time we found the main street, it was pouring rain. Ben and I ate at a little pizza place that was covered in dark wood paneling and neon beer signs. The light was fading and we could hear thunder from somewhere far off. When we finished and stepped outside, the yellow sodium streetlights made the smooth pavement glisten. There was lightning. Driving around, we found the video store in a shopping center, behind all the tourist-trap establishments of the main street.

It was called "Dial M for Movies" and it sat between a Stop & Shop and a discount liquor store. I loved everything about it. Especially, I loved that it was an independent video store with a DVD copy of David Cronenberg's *Crash* in stock, nestled into a strip mall in Madison, Connecticut. We walked in and, as Ben browsed the video games, I went to the counter. "Hi. I called earlier. You've got a movie back there for me," I said. I lowered my voice a little and put my hands down, leaning in. "*Crash*?"

"Cult classic," he said, rustling around in a bin on the floor. He handed me the case.

"You know, I called two dozen places before I called here, came down from New London. Nobody else even knew what I was talking about."

"That's a damn shame," he said. "Spader's good in this one." I smiled and took their business card. Ben and I went next door to buy beer and wine.

J. G. Ballard died last year, the last of his many imagined deaths. He had slaughtered the world several times over in his writing and he was an old man, so it wasn't exactly a surprise. Still, when I heard, I began the process of finishing the pack of cigarettes in my pocket, making calls to every video store I could find in search of the movie version of his novel Crash and making further calls to find a ride. Eventually, I got through to my friend Ben, who agreed to drive me an hour outside New London, where we both attended college, on the condition that I buy him dinner. "I'm going to order something very expensive," he said. "You owe me money." When he drove up to my dorm in his yellow Jeep, he called out the window, "Why are we doing this, again?"

"Because, for once, there's a movie I can't steal off the Internet," I said, climbing up into the passenger seat.

When David Foster Wallace died, the year before, I had people to get drunk with, reading aloud from his books. In my life, though, I had never met anyone else who even knew who Ballard was. What could I say? His writing was scattered around my mind and my bookshelves, but what could I say? At least I could share the movie with someone. Anyway, in a strange way, the film is less troubling than Ballard's prose. It floats on the surface. It doesn't threaten anyone.

With a bottle of wine and the film in hand, I climbed back into Ben's truck, and we started back home. We slid past the backs of old industrial buildings, little patches of forest dotted between the sprawl, two rivers, a water tower. Places like this bring out the worst in people. Many of the towns we passed through were half empty, places for New Yorkers to summer in. The others had once been fishing villages, mill towns. I called Zoe from somewhere on the highway, but got her voice mail. I texted her "Come to my room at 10. We've got a wake to go to," and hoped she'd respond.

She never did, but at 10 I heard shoes squeak in the hall and then she was standing in my doorway, soaking wet. Strings of long blond hair hung from her head. She was tall, taller than I, with wide hips and a soft face. She was wearing a gray hoodie and blue sweatpants, almost uniformly darkened from the rain. "Jesus. Come in," I said.

Maybe, one day, I'll tell the story about the night I set her up to fuck my friend, in a room full of people who all knew what was going on and cringed when they thought I wasn't looking; or, of the final time she stood me up when, even though I had spent most of the night with another girl, I sat and waited in my room for her till the sun came up and I finally drank half a bottle of gin in bed before passing out. Of course, I could also tell the stories of all the times she told me she was bad for me or said that she felt so fucking guilty. Of course I could. Suffice it to say, I loved her though I knew I shouldn't have.

"So, why did you go where you went?" she asked, out of her hoodie and wrapped in my jacket.

"Madison," I said. "Halfway between here and New Haven."

"Ooh, I've been to New Haven!" she said. "So, why did you go all that way?"

"Because a writer named J. G. Ballard died," I said. "A science fiction writer, one of my favorites." I felt like a librarian, or a museum tour guide, or a father leading a child through a museum. She was sitting on my bed. "So, Ben took me to Madison because it was the only place I could find this." I held up the DVD and she cocked her head. "This is my mourning process." I tossed her the DVD along with my old paperback copy of *Crash* and started to uncork the wine.

Ballard, the great anatomist, must have seen it coming, but I didn't. He seemed ageless. He, the great futurist, must have seen it coming for a long time. But, I'm not a futurist.

I'm not a futurist, because I'm terrible at augury. Show me entrails, I see entrails. I can't do prophecy, neither can I play chess nor pick up women in bars. Ballard was a futurist because he knew me, in 1973, better than I knew myself in 2006. The first time I picked up *Crash* I felt a dozen perversions blossom out of my subconscious. The fascination and vague terror I had always felt at the suburban sprawl of my childhood came into sharp focus. Narratives are powerful things, where identity is concerned.

And when a futurist dies, the tragedy is that we lose access to all the possible futures they imagined for us. Our only connection, afterward, is through the arcane procedure like literary interpretation, like reading the flight of birds or throwing the I Ching, as Ballard must have as a child in Shanghai. Like it or not, we live in one of Ballard's futures; a little apocalyptic, bent by technology. It would have been nice to have him around a while longer.

"So, what's it about?" she said.

"Well, he wrote a lot of real sci-fi, but this isn't quite that. It's not about the future, exactly, it's... about the way technology changes us," I heard myself giving the gloss explanation. What was I supposed to say? 'It's about perverts, darling, and violence.' But she was sitting up and looking straight at me like a good pupil. I owed it to her to explain, even if I didn't tell her just what was in my mind at the time. "He mostly wrote about the end of the world, till his wife died—"

"How did she die?" she interrupted.

"I'm not sure," I said and laughed. "Anyway, after, his writing got much stranger. He wrote a collection of short stories, then this." She was thumbing through the book, full of my highlights and margin notes, the pages warped from my sweaty hands holding it for hours on end as I read. "It's about... violence. And sex. And, uh, broken bodies," I trailed off. "It's fairly fucked up." I didn't want it to sound like a warning. She didn't say anything, sitting with her back straight and her eyes fixed on me as I looked around and tried to avoid her gaze.

I poured us each a glass of wine and moved over to the couch. She sat down on the other end of the big black sofa and I switched off the lamp, letting the room fill with blue LCD light. I pressed play and for a long while, I watched her face instead of the screen. There's fucking in the first seconds of the film and within five minutes, a car accident, which sets off the action. Zoe sat with her hands at her face and squirmed, but she didn't look away from the screen, except to take quick sips of wine. Eventually, I touched her shoulder, and she slid over next to me. We started to whisper.

She said she wanted "Catharine Ballard," Deborah Unger. "She's too skinny," I said. "All bones."

"That's what a pelvis should look like," she said. By this time I had my arms wrapped around her. Occasionally, she touched her lips to my forearm. I was trembling and practically growling. It's not about an absence of desire. It's just a transfer of desire, away from the body.

I had always wanted "Vaughan." He's bald and pale in the movie, more scars than skin. My own body is laced with scars. On my face and left arm, the marks of a childhood injury. Across my back, a long scar left from a car accident in my teen years. I have tiger stripes on my stomach and hips, stretch marks faded to an iridescent ivory color. Finally, rows and rows of tidy scars all down my thighs. They elicit a very specific kind of disgust from most people. I've never found anything sexy about them, symbols as they are of my clumsiness, my gluttony and instability. Except Zoe had a deep, wide scar down her right thigh from a surgery, and I loved it.

"Here it comes," I said. Toward the end of the movie, Vaughan's head dips below the dashboard of his big black Lincoln, to the lap of the fictional Ballard. My breath caught, and she turned her head. My hand went straight down the front of her pants and I could feel how wet she was. Her head fell back into my chest and my mouth went to her neck. It's not about gender, or sex for that matter. She pulled my hand away.

"I want to see the rest of it," she said. We watched the final minutes in silence, and I had a wide smile across my face. When it finally ended, she was sitting up, sorting out our glasses and the wine. I sat up, too, and turned off the TV set. "I told you it was fucked up," I said.

"I liked it," she said

"I'm glad." I said.

"It was... rough," she said, and I immediately kissed her. I was already sitting at the edge of the couch, one hand on the back of her neck. I cupped my other hand over her pussy and lifted her with me as I stood. She came up with a wave of her arms, planting her feet to catch her balance. It must have looked absurd. "Oh! Okay." she said, still steadying herself. We stood like that for a while. I had a good hold, grinding my hand into her, pinching the nipple of her left breast. She was breathing into my neck. She stepped back, and I lifted her shirt over her head. I kissed her again, hard, and turned us toward the bed. It was a very small room.

"Down," I said, as I pressed my hand flat against her chest and pushed. She fell back with her arms still at her sides and bounced a little when she hit the mattress. I'm sure I just stood there, looking at her splayed out on the bed. Her breasts were small and dipped a little, but on her back they settled out to the sides, opening up her chest. When we were both on the bed, my hands found her tits and my mouth went to hers. She had already undone the button and zipper of her pants. I pushed them down and shoved two fingers into her. She gasped and I hooked my fingers, pressing into the soft spot just behind her pelvic bone and pulling her body toward mine. My other hand went to her throat. The heel of my palm pressed on her clit. Her eyes were open very wide. At first, I wasn't so much gripping her neck as leaning on it, pressing my weight down and watching the mattress dip. Then my thumb grazed her windpipe.

"Fuck. Yes," she said.

I started to speak, but nothing was there. I kept my fingers moving, bent over, and kissed her. I pressed my thumb down and felt the change in her breath. I bit her lip. Three fingers. Behind me, the wind rattled the windows in their frames. Her legs were so smooth they shone, and they flew all over the bed, bending and straightening, up and down. Her arms were still, hands gripping the edges of the mattress. All the muscles in her neck tightened. She came, and we lay like that for a while, my hand still around her neck and my fingers still inside her. She was breathing hard and finally her hand was running up and down my chest.

I knelt between her open legs and pulled my shirt off. She was propped up on her elbows. Her breasts hung and there were small folds on her stomach, where she bent. She looked so beautiful, watching me so intently. Something in me was breaking. My cock was only half-hard. I undid my belt and awkwardly slid each leg out of my pants while I was still on my knees. I forgot that the condoms were in the drawer of my desk, on the other side of the room. My socks were still on. We'd had bad sex before, usually because we were drunk, but I was suddenly very aware of all the times she hadn't touched me when I greeted her, how she kept her hands off me. She told me once that she didn't care what I looked like, but I ran over the list of other guys she was with. They were all lithe, some attractive. I knew a few of them and she talked about them all, often. They were the reason we had gotten together, the first time; sitting up with her and listening to her complaints about one of them, wondering aloud whether what she was doing was wrong. Of course not, I told her. I was suddenly very aware of my body, and it felt unwieldy.

"Is something wrong?" she said.

"I don't know," I said. "I..." I couldn't find words, again. "Why don't you suck me off?" It wasn't my voice, all false bravado and edge.

"Fine," she sighed, and my heart sank. "Slide down." I laid back and raised my arms over my head. I must have crossed my wrists. I always do, lying down like that. She curled up alongside me, knees tucked up to her chest, her arm stretched across my stomach. I felt her take the head of my cock in her mouth and slide her hand under my balls, gripping tightly. As she lowered her mouth on my cock, I could feel her tongue run across them. It was bright for a second, off somewhere. My hand found her ass, slid up across her back, gripped her shoulder. I could feel her tongue grazing over my balls each time my cock slid into the back of her mouth. I could feel her lips, her teeth. I could feel her spine under my fingers.

I felt her other hand on my thigh. Four fingers, sliding back and forth on four perfect, parallel scars. I could hear rain coming in the windows, then. My hand came down on top of hers, and I interlaced our fingers, bringing both hands to the mattress. "Don't mind the scars," I said. I felt her lips, her tongue, slide up and down a few more times.

"I can't do this," she said, sitting up. I was still laying back, and she rolled to her side, putting her head on my chest. My cock was still hard.

"Can't do what?"

"All this emotional stuff," she said. I could see the sky outside, blurred through the wet screens, and it was green tinted. "How did you get them?"

"An X-Acto knife," I said. "And if we're going to have this conversation, I need to put pants on." I walked across the floor, covered with our clothes, and found a pair of shorts. I lay back down and slid my arm underneath her. Her leg crossed over mine.

The Johns

Audacia Ray

I am coming.

I can't be coming. I'm fighting it, and that's making it worse. I am trying to fake not having an orgasm. I wonder if he can tell.

I've never had an orgasm creep up on me like this before, like a bug up my spine, with no foreshadowing whatsoever. This orgasm isn't inspired even a little bit by desire; it's a purely mechanical reaction.

I feel a little sick to my stomach when I realize exactly what sensation has brought me to this unfortunate climax: the friction of a very fat man's matted belly hair on my clit. This man I am on top of is the most repulsive person I've ever allowed to touch me. Sheer physics won't allow him to be on top of me. In fact, I am not entirely sure how it is that he will get back up from his supine position.

This man is my john. This orgasm and the wave of revulsion that follows quickly on its heels and makes my skin turn cold makes him my last client in my short career as an escort.

♦

"I would never date a guy who sees sex workers." Jenny is wide-eyed and disapproving as she sucks on her cigarette. "I mean, never." She's really grossed out by the guys she hustles money from at the shiniest and best gentlemen's clubs in Manhattan. They're pathetic, in her estimation. Nothing like her bike messenger boyfriend, who she met at the bike collective, where they rebuild vintage fixed gears and then ride around the city on dumpster dumpster-diving missions.

In the gown clubs, Jenny is decadent and polished, all glitter and sweet yummy stripper smells, hair flips, and stilettos. She might have a heart of gold—after all, she spends her time out of the club working on social justice projects and uses her money to fund the art projects of the people she shares a Bushwick squat with—but in the club, you wouldn't know it.

My boundaries are fierce, too, but I draw them differently than Jenny does. Sharing intimacy with johns is gross and bad—that's why I quit doing full service. I thought I was in control: I invented this character of a nice, twenty-something New Yorker who happens to be an escort. But sex is always surprising and my body reminded me, with a strong hit of anarchy, that try as I might, I'm not always the person in the driver's seat.

I've neatly excised the potential for inconvenient sexual pleasure from my job. Now I giggle evasively when my massage clients, disappointed in my panties-on approach, ask the smarmy and predictable question, "Who massages you?" The answer is my boyfriend John (yes, capital-jay-John, because you just can't make this shit up), who knows what I do and accepts it mostly because he's a john himself. Jenny is tickled pink about the name nonsense when she meets John formally and actually insists on seeing his driver's license. She's sneering mostly because she's put two and two together—when his work is going well, he's a regular in her club, where the girls refer to him as "the hot punk dude."

♦

I'm sitting on the bed in his one-bedroom apartment—it's the only place to sit, really—bent at the waist, my garter belt cutting into my middle, making it hard to breathe. Actually, it's probably not the garter belt that's making me feel claustrophobic in my body; it's the crazy amount of cocaine coursing through my veins.

He doesn't want to get off tonight, and I'm relieved. He does, however, want to watch me in heels and stockings. "This can be arranged," I told him earlier on the phone from my place in Brooklyn. I packed my bag, careful to put my stilettos in plastic baggies baggies so they wouldn't tear the stockings as I folded them neatly into place.

Some sex workers specialize in clients who like to party or ski or whatever the euphemism for cocaine is these days. I'm not into that. I have boundaries: no intimacy, panties on, and no drugs.

But for John—I bend the rules. Well, not really. Again: he isn't my john, though he is a john. "Our relationship" evolved into this thing in the room between us through lunchtime hookups in hourly hotels with no comforters on the beds; a practical measure that is so symbolic as to be absurd. Our relationship is fluid, which sounds nice but in practice means that it conforms to the containers it is put in, like in middle school science when you're learning about the different kinds of matter. We could shape these flasks and beakers ourselves, being creative and theoretically freethinking people. However, our containers are the shape of hooker and john, slightly remixed to look like a relationship.

And though I have lots of rules that protect me from the lurking harms and humiliations a sex worker can be subjected to by johns as a matter of course, I throw these rules out for John and others like him who aren't paying me for my time.

We misbehave, and we misbehave at each other. I let him do things to me that I would never let a john do. And I don't even mean anal. I mean the real messy stuff: no call, no show. Share me with friends. Snort coke off my toes. And in turn, I'm a lazy lover. I'm frequently not in the mood. Sometimes I fake it, and, worse yet, sometimes I'm not sure whether I'm faking it or not.

Some sex workers say that their johns made them hate men, but I like my johns a lot more than I like other men. My johns don't ever disrespect me the way John does. Or rather, they do, and I don't hesitate to show them the door, while in my so-called romantic life, the fluidity of our arrangement means that I can't get a handle on anything.

Answer

Douglas Wolk

THERE'S AN AWFUL CALCULUS that happens very quickly when your boss asks if she can suck your cock. It goes like this:

Well, come on, what were you thinking would happen when she said oh, you should totally stay at my place when you're in town, I love having guests, and you said sure, I'd love to stay with you? And also you really do like her a lot, you think she's funny and smart and pretty, you've been firing messages back and forth for months about work and nonwork things, don't deny that you hoped more than a little that maybe something might happen. Maybe it will bring you closer together—you know you'd like that, being closer to her. Maybe it will make you less lonely, maybe it will help something in her that's sad that you didn't know about, maybe it will just feel good, maybe it will be a crazy secret you can laugh about later or pretend you're laughing about it while you treasure the memory or pretend you're laughing about it while you're trying to scrub it out of your brain. Maybe she'll give you more and better gigs. Maybe she thinks you owe her this for giving you lots of gigs, and this is some sort of conscious or unconscious power trip. Maybe this is just the way it goes in this city, everybody is fucking all the time stresslessly, it's like if she asked if she could get you something to drink, get over it. Maybe, hey, this is the kind of shit that women go through all the time, how do you like a taste of it, cry yourself a river.

Isn't this the way it goes sometimes, between bosses and their employees? Is it maybe not a bad idea to work out whatever this is between you? Are you worried about it because it's wrong? Could you be an exception? Is the wrongness kind of hot? Is it theoretically kind of hot but in fact you're finding it isn't, not at all? Is it nice to be appreciated and desired anyway? Is the reason you're worrying about this just that it's theoretically wrong because of the financial power dynamic but actually that part doesn't matter and you should just be running the calculus on the interpersonal level? Is it actually going to hurt you economically if you say no, or if you say yes, or oh come on you know that she is scrupulously honest on a business level and will treat you fairly no matter what happens right now. Right? Again: right?

Also, isn't it sort of sweet of her to ask? Brave, actually, to ask right up front for what she wants? For what you really ought to admit to yourself that you want? How does that bluntness charge the air? How might it affect what happens next? What's her own calculus that led her to say that (or to say that as opposed to asking in some less power-dynamics-charged are-we-going-to-do-this? way) or did it just slip out of her, one of those rogue blurts of desire?

Is there any way to go back from this moment? How much does she trust you? How vulnerable has she just made herself? How badly might you hurt her if you say the wrong thing?

If you say no, what does that say about you: that you are fussy about exactly the way your little fantasy is going to go and won't have it on her terms, that you hinted that you were available to her just to bring this out of her, just so you could turn her down, just so you could have that power over her? Isn't that kind of sick, and don't you want to correct that impulse in yourself? Would that be punishing her by doing what other people have done to you, and isn't that even more messed up? If you say no, are you fundamentally being a guy wrong?

If you say yes, what does that say about you: that you want to give yourself to her, that you want to let her let you be the one she's kneeling down in front of, that you will say yes to anyone, that you will say yes to her in particular even though it's not quite what you had in mind? That you are on vacation so you're playing by different rules today? Is this going to make her like you more? Is it going to make you like her more? Is it going to make her like herself more? Is it going to make you like yourself more? Is there going to be shame involved either way? Yours? Have you earned it already?

If this situation goes really wrong, are you going to be able to make it into a funny story, one of those things where you find yourself in a situation that totally wasn't your fault at all, where all the comedy comes out of your being a wide-eyed naïf who's stumbled into someone's den? Or are you going to face up to your own complicity in it? If it goes really wrong are you still going to be able to be friends with her, your cool funny boss who gives you so much easy work and values your opinions and talks to you all the time? Can you make yourself agree that whatever happens it's going to be something that you consented to of your own free will? Can you for once own your decision, your attraction, your command over what happens in response to something that she didn't try to do, she asked, and that it was within her rights to ask?

If you pause for too long before you answer her—and by now probably two whole seconds have gone by—what does that say about you: that you're shocked or angry, that you have a gut reaction that you're trying to overcome, that you can't permit yourself pleasure, that you're going to pretend what you're thinking isn't what you know it really is? Fucking answer.

And so you say *sure*! trying to load a lot into that one syllable: that this is okay, that it was admirably daring of her to ask that and of course you're thinking along the same lines, that the tension's been broken and now we're at the fun part.

And after thirty seconds or so she stops and says "I shouldn't do this, I can't do this, you need to go, don't you have somewhere else you can stay"—she's crying by this point—"you've got all these women." She's crying and talking as if she doesn't know where she is but is trying to act like she does, and things start to click into position in your head—the lyrics written in lipstick on her bathroom door, the big snifter of wine, the chilly little guest bed. "You know I pay you the best rate of anybody who works for me," she says, not even trying not to cry. That might be one of the worst things she could say at that moment, but you say things you don't think will hurt her as much as they do, too.

And you fly home and between the emails where you're both dealing with your normal business with each other in the normal way, normal normal normal, which you'll keep doing until her bosses' money runs out, and the other sequence of measured emails where the two of you are trying to calmly process what went on (because really it was stupid of you to even imagine she'd deal with you in anything other than an honest and reasonable way, she genuinely is a grown-up about this, probably more than you), there's an email from her where she's just cut and pasted the phrase "I'm sorry" a few hundred times, "I'm sorry I'm sorry I'm sorry I'm sorry I'm sorry." Yeah, you too, but what were you supposed to say?

The Apartment

Diana Vilibert

"I HAVE A GIRLFRIEND," Jack mumbles into his t-shirt as I peel it off his body. A giant cross covers his rib cage and I think I see Jesus peeking out of his chest hair.

Jack's hands are frozen in place, cupping my ass as I sit on his lap. He waits for my answer. "Is that okay?"

"Sure," I say, "It's okay with me." The words dribble feebly out of me, like drool, and I look at Jack's mouth instead of his eyes. "This isn't really my apartment. It's my ex-boyfriend's."

I had met Jack an hour earlier, between the Bedford and the Lorimer stop on the L train, on my way back from a bar. I was drunk and slouched in a seat. My eyelids were drooped like half-open curtains when he sat down next to me, straddling a guitar case between his knees. I notice his tattooed forearm first, scaling my eyes up his body, his uniform of black skinny jeans and a black v-neck t-shirt clinging to his thin frame. When I look up, I see that he was staring back at me. His eyebrows smile at me, and I turn away quickly, pretending to look for something in my purse.

"Man," he says, shaking his head. "I can't believe it, I can't believe it." He speaks quietly, as if to himself, but I feel his eyes on the side of my face. "Man," he repeats. "Fucking Michael Jackson. Did you hear he died today?" he asks, directing his monologue at me. I nod. Jack repeats almost everything twice. "I mean, his music, fuck." he trails off. "I was listening to 'Billie Jean' this morning. This morning! And now he's dead. Now he's fucking dead."

He tells me the story of how he heard the news, and I half-listen, nodding when it seems appropriate. When his voice cracks, he shakes his head and apologizes for crying, even though he isn't. I'm afraid he might start, so I grab his forearm and ask about his tattoos. As he talks, my fingers trace the ink around his wrist. When he asks if I have any Michael Jackson songs on my iPod, I say no, but that I do at my apartment.

We stumble the two blocks from the subway, and I shut the door behind us and push him against the lime-green kitchen wall. Kitty kibble crunches under my heels as I press my breasts up against him, unbuttoning his jeans. His lips find mine, and we kiss the way people kiss when they know they're about to fuck. We grope at each other like teenagers, and I lead him to the couch. I straddle his lap and reach over to the computer, pulling up iTunes and pressing play on "Billie Jean." I consider "Dirty Diana" but decide against it.

I don't know why I tell him that it's Alex's apartment. I regret it as I hear myself say the words, and they hang between us like a fog. We pause our frantic groping and Jack stares at me, silent, his lips parting slightly as if about to say something. "I'm house-sitting while he's in rehab," I explain. I pick at the cigarette burn on the couch cushion. "He's a heroin addict," I answer before he asks.

When Alex and I ended things, he asked if I would stay at his place and cat-sit until he got back from rehab. I pretended to think about it, packed a few duffel bags of clothes, and settled in. In fear of the breakdown I would surely have if I slept in the bedroom, I slept on the couch at first. I made it twelve days. On the thirteenth, I looked in the kitchen sink and saw the bowls and glasses perched precariously on top of each other in the same exact arrangement I had left them in six months ago and started crying—a big, ugly, gasping cry that felt larger than my face.

"Don't worry," I assure Jack. "This is cool. I'm allowed to have people over." Alex had left me with a short list of instructions and phone numbers before departing across the country. He told me to make myself at home, to have friends over and even men, if I wanted. Each time I replayed his words in my head, my face flushed hot from his indifference.

Jack doesn't respond, and I imagine he's wondering if this is what he gets for picking up a girl on the L train at 3 a.m. I stare down at the hole on the couch. Jack moves his hands up my back and starts to undo the halter tie on my dress. He asks how long we dated, and when I say a year, he looks surprised. "I loved him," I shrug.

"That's rough," he finally says. "I mean, I drink a lot, I'm probably an alcoholic, but I'd never touch that shit." I nod and reassure him that it wasn't that bad, but as I watch Jack's eyes scan the space around us, I can tell he doesn't believe me.

I have grown not to notice the dusty tint of this apartment. It was, like Alex, the vaguely muted version of the life I wanted to have with him, the promise of what could be trapped just below the surface of what really was. The wood floor is dirty, stray cat litter pebbles trailing into the kitchen, home to a table full of cat food, an empty refrigerator, a handful of bowls and glasses (no plates), and a box of plastic utensils. In the living room, a permanent chalky white stains the computer desk where Alex used to sit and dice up speedballs with the precision of a master chef, his long thin fingers gripping one edge of a plastic card.

"Take off your bra," Jack orders, "let me see those tits." I cringe when he says "tits." I do as I'm asked, and suggest the bedroom, telling him I need to pee and that I'd meet him in there. I close the bathroom door behind me, kicking off my heels. I switch on the light and open the medicine cabinet, a force of habit I picked up when I suspected Alex was lying to me about his drug use. I'm not sure why I bothered, as if a heroin addict would leave his secret stash behind a smudged mirror, in between floss and expired Pepto-Bismol.

I quickly swipe on some deodorant and walk out of the bathroom. Then I step in something that squishes under the ball of my foot. "Fuck!" I yell, not loud enough for Jack to hear but loud enough for the cats, perhaps. I reach for the paper towels.

When I walk into the bedroom, Jack asks if everything is okay. "Sorry," I say. "I stepped in cat vomit." Jack nods. "Okay." If he's bothered, he hides it well. He makes a low *mmm* sound and pulls me onto the bed by the hand. He starts to kiss my face, and his previous fervor has died down. He kisses my shoulders softly, and his breathing is deep but steady. "You don't have to be so gentle," I say.

He grins and smacks my ass hard and says he wants to go down on me, pushing me off him and onto my back. He slides off my boyshorts and kisses my thighs until I squirm and tell him to stop teasing. He listens and I feel his hot breath travel up my inner thighs. I close my eyes and let my legs fall open. I come quickly, and he slides back up the bed, lips curling into a small self-satisfied smile. He pulls me against him, and I'm not sure if we're done, so I ask if I should get a condom. He says he'd feel bad. "My girlfriend..." he trails off. He kisses my forehead and absentmindedly gropes me for a few minutes, until we see sunlight making its way through the window above us. "I live with her," he adds, and I tell him he should probably go home then.

I wrap the sheets around me and follow him to the living room, and I stand near the door and watch him get dressed, handing him a lint brush when he's done. "Cat hair," I say. He does his front and I help him with his back, and he kisses me on the cheek. I prop the door open and he thanks me for playing Michael Jackson and I thank him for listening to me talk about Alex.

I listen to his footsteps until there's silence and lock the door behind him. It occurs to me now, that when Alex returns home, I'll tell him everything just like I always have.

Crouching down on the floor, I refill the water and food bowl for the cats and they scamper over, out of hiding. I stand in the middle of the kitchen and watch them eat, waiting until they're done before walking toward the bedroom. I pull the comforter and fitted sheet off the bed and shove the pillows on the floor. I shut the door even though I'm alone and lie down on the bare mattress. My eyes are still open when my alarm sounds two hours later.

Parts of a Whole

Danny Vitolo

I'M JOLTED BY THE UNMISTAKABLE SOMATIC MEMORY of her grabbing my hair and pulling my dripping face from her crotch, bit-gag baring my teeth. My audible and involuntary grunt rings in my ears while I watch the cornfield blur out the window. I used to relish this anticipatory period between my city and hers, winding myself up on fantasy. I'm surprised by how vivid my discomfort is. The chrome clasps and leather straps have dissolved into silverware and television and awkward, absent silence. Nothing's been the same, except we both still need each other.

I was new to town, leaving behind a small city full of bad memories, and she was my first date. There was a decade between us. She had a primary partner and was looking for somebody to augment their relationship. We joked about who seduced who. Our hands would roam over each other's limbs during artist lectures and gallery visits. Sex was bookended by discussions of the intersections between feminism, art history, antiracism. She demonstrated time and again that my nipples were buttons attached to my cock. That respect is of the utmost importance.

I'd convinced myself I was broken. That the years of drunken discarnate sex ruined me. Sober sex was awkward and aware. I'd make it about the other person. I'd occupy my mind with what they wanted. Better that than worry about not responding properly or wondering what to do with my hands. Better that than deal with the lack of interest my body was trying desperately to make me notice.

I'd found a surprising amount of comfort in light bondage during my early sexual history, but I hadn't really thought anything of it as anything but an addition to plain old vanilla sex. Certainly, it hadn't crossed my mind that it would be a way past my discomfort or that it could fill a craving I hardly knew I had.

Having been happily single for a few years I took comfort in the fact that the day-to-day grind of a relationship was burdened by her committed, live-in partner. I could count on one hand the number of times I met him, and, honestly, the time we spent together was awkward. I was glad to see her weekly; our relationship was fulfilling and more than enough to keep me satisfied. It was fascinating to watch a woman who was so confident about her ability to draw pleasure from pain. It was illuminating to see how she arranged her life to handle the complexities of multiple partnerships.

She instructed me to be silent, to be motionless. She demanded my attention be focused not only on her but also on my own body under her touch. She fed off my lust, the tension and release of my muscles. I relished my own acceptance of and appreciation for such close attention. Never before had I felt so taken care of. There were hogties and hoods and paddles. The feeling of her vagina contracting orgasmically around my penis, my body motionless and ecstatic. The ability to focus on sensations instead of memories. The room to explore.

After a few months and much talk of love, she took a job in a nearby city. The distance wasn't difficult; I loved getting away for a weekend. Everything was spectacular for a few months. She was happy. We were happy. When her primary partner died I didn't know what to do. There's no way to fill that space. It is not my place to fill that space. But what is my place? She can't talk about me to her coworkers. She can't explain why she's dating somebody when the man she calls her husband just passed. She's falling apart. She's fallen apart. But she's still moving. I'm afraid to bring anything up. I'm afraid to talk about him. I'm afraid to ignore him. I'm afraid she's going to leave.

We will do household chores together; we'll watch TV. We'll sleep in the same bed. I'll gaze at the toy cabinet. The same DVDs over and over. They help her fall asleep, and they're calming when she inevitably wakes up from a nightmare. I'll pet her cat, transfixed by my own enervated response. I'll laugh when I'm nervous. I won't know how to talk about how this is affecting me. How can you say, "Enough about you. Let's talk about me?" I'll dismiss my feelings. I'll lose myself. The pain is crushing, isolating. Even before all this, I never knew what she saw in me.

Absolution

K. Bridgeman

SOMETIMES I DON'T WANT TO STOP. *Sometimes, in the middle of completely sane, rational conversations, I want to lunge at her and sink my teeth into her chest just to feel the heat of her skin and the arch of her back. I want something rough, because I know she'll fight back. I want to dig my fingers into her skin and have her pull my head back and bite my shoulder, writhing and twisting against me until neither of us is sure whether we want to break free or fuck. I want all the softness of her breast in the space where it meets her sternum to be encapsulated by my seeking lips, and when she moans I want it to sound like the scraping of lust from the sharp corners of her desire, forced out and guttural. I want her to hate me while I push my knee between her thighs, and to tell me I'm a fucking bastard in between the grunts elicited from having her nipples bitten and sucked. I want angry red claw marks on my back from her nails, and my t-shirt stretched and disfigured when she tears it off of me and thrusts her hand down the front of my jeans. I want to be so smug and sure of my own superiority and how wet she is and how well I'm going to fuck her that I have no time to react when she suddenly flips over and pins me. To be so surprised that all I can do is savor the sting when she slaps the smirk right off my face. Except it won't leave that easily. And while she's demanding my obedience and tracing sharp patterns on my skin, I'll still thrust my hips up into her, and mouth off, because I can. For now. Until she takes away my control. Until she has me on my knees begging to be fucked or sucking her cock, or completely exposed and being paddled or whipped. I want to have control wrenched from my closed fist and then be made to like it. I want her to fuck me until I scream or sing or come so hard the sheets are soaked and my body barely lets go of her fist. And when it's over, and I lie shuddering on the floor, she'll pick me up and kiss me softly, and my fingers will wind themselves into her hair or rest against her chest so I can feel the way her heart pounds. And then she'll let me fuck her.*

"It's not about me," she said matter-of-factly as she closed her laptop and stowed it away next to the bed.

"Parts of it are about you," I ventured in a tone I hoped was nonchalant. "The line about the space on her chest? That's totally you. I think that's a really sexy part of your body."

She ignored me. "It's about her, isn't it?"

I shifted my weight uncomfortably. "It's not about any one person; it's about a lot of women. Besides, mostly it's about me... what I want. You know? We've talked about this."

"Don't lie to me; you know that just makes it worse."

"I'm not..."

"Did you fuck her?"

"Look, it's really not like that. I swear. It's not even a big deal. We just write together."

"You're writing with her?" Her voice broke little, and was suddenly small. "... That was supposed to be ours."

"Baby," I pleaded as I crawled over the rumpled ocean of sheets towards her, "Please, please don't cry."

As I arrived on the other side of the bed, she turned to face me, and my stomach dropped. Her eyes were cold and dull, evidence that, for the first time, the distance between us was actually as wide as I'd believed it to be all that time I'd been walking away from us. It was terrifying. I scrambled for a fix, but the more I tried to explain, the further away she seemed. There was nothing left to say, so instead we crawled into bed and stayed there, clinging to each other as though the world were about to end. Neither of us was sure what would happen if we weren't holding hands.

I don't know exactly what triggered the change, but at some point the cuddling segued into "I want your cock" with startling rapidity. Lubed, hard, and properly adjusted, I entered her with a single stroke. With a snarl she bucked her hips against me and sunk her nails into my chest as though she could rip my skin off. My face hardened and I began in earnest, fucking her cunt like an open wound. Through gritted teeth she told me how she craved me and demanded I tell her just exactly how much I loved being inside her. We laid into each other, expressions of pleasure contorting into rage. She came quickly, the orgasm wracking her body like a building collapsing. Deep tremors and her cries enveloped me, sound rushing outward in a cloud of heat and fullness and despair.

After the spasms, the pulsing and panting, I waited for softness and permission to collapse into her, but it didn't come. Instead, she contemptuously spat, "Get off me." Unsure, but unwilling to disobey, I pulled out, rolled off, and lay beside her on the bed, waiting.

While she sat on the edge of the bed, pulling her tousled hair into a ponytail, I considered the contrast of a blue wall where it met the ceiling. I noticed for the thousandth time a splotch of that paint marring the white expanse above me. Despite my best efforts to divide the two neatly, the border was sloppy and inconsistent.

Her nails on my chest brought me crashing back to reality. When she raked across my nipples, I started and whimpered involuntarily, reaching to grab her wrist.

"Shut up," she snapped. "And do not touch me. No matter what."

To my horror, from the depths of my struggle for stillness, I began to laugh—giggles at first, chased by a smile erupting on my lips. Her fingers froze in their tracks.

"What's so funny?" she sneered, but I simply shook my head. I didn't know, couldn't have told her, and wasn't allowed to speak anyway. I struggled for control of my face, but failed miserably. Her palm connected with my cheek. She repeated the question, and again I didn't answer. Her hand came again, the sharp report of it ringing in my head, my room, and evidenced in the heat on my cheek. She got down low, close to my face, and her voice was dangerously quiet.

"If you don't stop laughing, I will not fuck you. That's a promise." She followed it up with a final ruthless blow.

Somewhat in shock, I considered for the first time that she truly wasn't playing. She really would stop, leave me hanging and destroy me in the process if I dared to disobey. She was someone new, someone I had never seen before, and I had no idea what she was capable of.

"On your knees." The order came, more barked than spoken. "You will not speak unless I tell you to. Do you understand?"

On all fours, facing the wall, my cock limp in its harness and my cunt exposed and dripping, I could do little more than nod. There was a momentary pause, then her nails bit into my back, and she began to paddle my ass in earnest. I grunted in pain, forcing myself to hold it together and gasped audibly when she sunk her teeth roughly into my flesh.

"You like telling me what to do?" Her questions punctuated the blows. "You like being in charge? Well I'm in charge now. And you're going to do whatever the fuck I tell you. FUCK. YOU."

The muscles in my thighs trembled, and I bit hard on my bottom lip to keep from whimpering. I deserved this; wasn't this exactly what I'd said I wanted? Now the spanking stopped, though the pattern of nails on skin did not, and she began to massage my aching clit with her free hand.

"You're going to come for me. I'm going to fuck you hard, and you're going to fucking come for me. You'd better fucking come."

I pressed into her palm, desperate for release and eager to please. In response she moved her fingers to the mouth of my cunt. She paused only momentarily, to wet them, then slid her whole fist into me. Her wrist rotations moved in sync with my gyrations, and soon I was bucking wildly against her. Peripherally I was aware of the looseness of the strap of my harness, the flapping of the leather and my skin, but I was so far gone that it would have been impossible to care.

The circles gave way to deep, angled thrusting, and as she picked up speed, I felt pangs of pain. I tried to fight through them, to keep going and make my body come for her, but instead I began to weep. Great, gasping sobs wracked my body as the nails on my back eased to a soothing touch. From within me, she emerged to wipe my tears and hush my cries.

"Shhh, shhh," came her gentle sighs, "Everything's going to be fine."

We lay there together, soaking in the lie, and as she held my trembling body and kissed my eyelids, she whispered tiny love songs in my ears.

"Audrey" from "Shoplifting from American Apparel"

Tao Lin

I THINK SHE OR HER GAY MALE FRIEND commented on my blog—in early 2008 maybe—and I clicked one of their profiles, looked at their group-blog, saw pictures of her, and thought she seemed pretty and nice. She added me on Facebook maybe two months later. I looked at her tagged photos and liked them. Some time later she uploaded a YouTube video of herself in an all-pink outfit dancing in her room to MTV or VH1. In the video she said "whoa" in a tone I liked. I commented that she should wear the all-pink outfit to my reading in November, 2008, in Florida, that she'd said—on Facebook, I think—she was attending.

The reading was at a vegan brunch buffet during a 3–4 day punk/folk music festival. I saw her standing in line for food and felt a little surprised that she had come (it was around 10:30 a.m.), that she had come alone apparently, and that she had "actually" worn the all-pink outfit. I read—to about twenty-five people—the beginning of *Shoplifting from American Apparel*, which I was still writing (the last ~25 percent of the book, published September, 2009, is the 3–4 day music festival in this essay), and noticed her standing behind a sofa staring at me with a calm facial expression. After I read she introduced herself. We did things with two other people until around 5:30 p.m. when she and I went alone to a free concert in a University of Florida building.

We sat against the back wall of the concert hall. At one point I drew a hamster and other things on her leg with an expensive-looking marker we had found on a table outside. At one point we "explored" the building by walking through hallways into empty rooms of different sizes. During most of these two–three hours we had neutral or serious facial expressions but were focused, whenever we said anything, on making jokes or amusing observations, I felt. There were sometimes one–five minutes of neither of us saying anything. There were maybe four–eight situations where it seemed like we could have kissed, or something, but we didn't touch each other during this time. Sometimes it felt like we were in an early 3D game like Mario 64, due to the hallways and empty rooms and us being mostly focused on mutely climbing and walking through structures unfamiliar to us. At one point there was a small opening in a structure and she walked maybe 100 feet away and I looked at her through the opening. It seemed fun in a manner that combined elements of "deadpan" and being five years old.

Around 8:30 p.m. we went into a wooded area. She sat in a plastic chair—not sure why it was there—facing a small lake, and I began massaging her shoulders. I don't remember what prompted me to do that. I don't remember feeling nervous while doing it. I looked at the moonlight on the lake thinking something like "the reflection of the moonlight on the surface of the lake" and maybe—in a manner of vague, idle, meaningless acknowledgment—something about the line from a Lorrie Moore short story: *if there were a lake, the moonlight would dance across it in conniptions*. At some point I noticed "Audrey" making body movements and little noises indicating, to me, that she liked what was happening, which encouraged me to do something. I didn't do anything for maybe two minutes, then kissed her while still standing behind the chair with my body bent. I moved, while still kissing her, to the front of the chair and she stood, and we kissed standing for maybe ten minutes. For some reason I keep imagining, as I type this, that she had a tongue ring. I think I'm being confused by her nipple rings (see below) and nose ring. I wonder if anyone losing interest in this essay has now regained interest after reading "nipple rings (see below)." Seems like now that I've foreshadowed nipple rings I can type anything and some people will continue reading. While kissing I felt maybe like we were in the movie *Garden State*, due to it being nighttime in a wooded area at a university neither of us attended, her being very pretty, and both of us being sort of "deadpan," among other reasons. I don't think I specifically referenced *Garden State* in my head at the time. I don't really like the movie *Garden State*, I think.

She asked if I wanted to go back to her car, and I said I did. We kissed for maybe five more minutes, then walked toward her car. I vaguely considered, for maybe ten seconds while leaving the forest, that we would "have sex" in her car—about ten minutes away—but when we got there, sitting in the passenger seat, I felt strongly that I didn't want to "move" at all in terms of touching her, while sensing that she also didn't feel like touching me currently. We seemed very unmotivated in a manner that seemed more mysterious or "dead," I think, than uninterested. I felt a little surprised how the tone had changed. On the way to the car there was "Colbert Stadium" or something and I had said it should be called "Stephen Colbert Stadium," which maybe affected us to feel unmotivated romantically/sexually. I'm not sure. After feeling "dead," then, for maybe twenty seconds, I suddenly felt that I really wanted to sit with her in a dark restaurant eating fries while sometimes hugging/kissing and maybe drinking one beer. I asked if she was hungry and if she wanted to eat. She said she wasn't and something like "not really" or "no," and I felt scared that she didn't say "yes" or something like "I could eat," because previously, the entire day, she had only expressed "eager" interest in doing more things. Now she seemed to be directly conveying, I felt, that she wanted to "get rid of me." In retrospect I feel that she probably wanted to go somewhere private to do sexual things instead of a restaurant.

I think I have a "low sex drive," which combined with feeling nervous/shy around most people makes it so in almost every initial sexual situation I seem to be "just sitting there," waiting for the other person to do something.

I idly looked at her CDs as she drove through Gainesville. After maybe fifteen minutes she asked if I wanted to go to Chris's house (earlier I had said I was staying at Chris's house, on a sofa on a school bus in his backyard) and I said I did. It was maybe 10:00 p.m. We parked and walked toward the house and through a gate into the backyard. We passed the school bus and sat side by side on a wooden bench inside a sort of giant tent—two sides and the top were enclosed—for maybe fifteen minutes, saying things with thirty–ninety seconds of silence in between. At one point she touched my head, then stopped when I was unresponsive (staring ahead while maybe holding my cell phone in my lap) and said "I can't do the massage thing." My main feeling at this point was maybe a calm, "literarily satisfying," slightly detached despair that I was somehow mostly focused, in each occurring moment, on contemplating "that"—less "why" than "that," less a questioning than an acknowledgment—I felt completely unmotivated to initiate physical contact, despite feeling very attracted to her and wanting on many levels for us to touch and kiss. It seemed like I had "given up" on life, as I sat there, not doing anything, but without any concrete reason. On some level I felt amused that I was calmly and consciously "not moving at all" while "ever aware" that I was in a situation where I could seemingly easily do something I had sort of fantasized (see below) about for maybe six months.

After maybe fifteen minutes she said she "guessed" she was going back to her friend's house. I said "okay" in a nonchalant tone while feeling depressed and anxious that she had said that. After a few minutes in which she didn't move to leave I began to feel calm. It seemed like she might not leave until something happened, which encouraged me to do something. I stood and walked a little and asked looking at the back of her head—she was still seated staring ahead—if she wanted to look at the inside of the bus. Here are the last few sentences of an earlier draft of *Shoplifting from American Apparel*:

> *They went on the bus. "Someone might be sleeping, is that a person," said Sam holding his cell phone's light to a mattress. "It's not a person, I think. Yeah, no one's here." He turned and stood facing Audrey. He could not see her face clearly. He hit his head against something coming down from the ceiling. He jumped a little and hit his head against the thing a few times. Audrey tried to hit the thing by jumping. She wasn't tall enough. She stood close to Sam and Sam felt her looking at him. She put her hands on Sam's waist then stood not touching him but looking at him.*

After that we kissed. I removed her jacket as we kissed. There was a mattress at the back of the bus with another mattress above it like a bunk bed. Someone might come on the bus, we knew, which made us move with more speed than normal, which maybe made things seem more "passionate" than normal, which seemed exciting. I was enjoying touching and kissing her and felt glad. We moved toward the mattress pretty quickly. She said "do you want to fuck me?" while we were still standing. I said "yes." I think I had removed—or had my hands under—her shirt. We sort of kneeled on the mattress. She asked if I had a condom. I said I didn't. She said "fuck" as I felt myself calmly continuing to touch her while strongly enjoying what was happening.

I don't clearly remember what chronologically happened after that. At one point I was sort of kneeling, and my penis was in her mouth. At another point she was on her back and I "discovered" she had nipple rings in both her nipples and "put" one ring in my mouth. It was a thin silver hoop. I think I had tried to remove her bra and was unsuccessful for five–ten seconds before she "did it herself." I feel aroused as I type this. I felt very sexually aroused by her. She had a pretty face in a manner that seemed playful and considerate and nondramatic in a sort of depressed/stoic manner. She was maybe 5'3" and 105 pounds. I had thought she might feel a little "bony," but she felt soft and warm in a manner that seemed healthy and sexy to me.

The first time my penis was in her mouth I think I stopped her after about fifty seconds, then put one finger and then two fingers in her vagina with us both lying on the mattress. At one point my penis was in her mouth as I was lying on my back. I don't remember if I orgasmed. I have a vague memory of "considering" orgasming onto the mattress, thinking that no one would be strongly negatively affected, due to different people sleeping there every night and no one showering, I think, during the 3–4 day music festival. I might have orgasmed onto her stomach and then cleaned the "cum" off her stomach with my boxer shorts, then put the boxer shorts in my pocket, then thrown them away later. I honestly don't remember. I might have not orgasmed. I'm pretty sure I didn't orgasm in her mouth and that my penis never entered her vagina. We were on the mattress for three–twenty minutes. I honestly can't remember if I "went down" on her briefly, or if I tried and she stopped me. I don't know if she orgasmed. I remember being focused on doing things with my fingers in a manner that I felt would be conducive to her orgasming.

I think probably I don't remember the "sexual parts" well (despite being sexually attracted to pictures and videos of her on the Internet and probably having masturbated to or idly fantasized about her three–fifteen times while still in New York City, before coming to Florida) because I wrote and then edited for hundreds of hours, and therefore thought about, and strengthened in my memory, the parts before and after the "sexual parts," for inclusion in *Shoplifting from American Apparel*. I didn't write the scene on the mattress on the bus in detail, I think, until this essay. It seems a little scary that most things in my life that I will remember, in ten years or something, will be the things I've chosen to write about, because sometimes it seems a little arbitrary what I choose to write about, sometimes I choose to write about things that didn't happen in concrete reality, and sometimes I don't choose to write about things that I want to remember because, among other reasons, they're difficult to write about or not "artistically satisfying" to write about. But I'm also glad about this "side effect" of writing because it seems like a clear and desirable reason, among other reasons, to write—to strengthen my memory of certain things.

After we finished we lay sort of next to each other without touching except maybe the sides of our arms. She seemed averse, at this point, to us holding each other, which confused me a little. We started putting on clothes after one of us said something about being nervous someone might come on the bus. I asked when she got her nipple rings. I think she said "last summer." I think I said I liked them. She apologized in a concerned tone for smelling and said she didn't usually smell. I had not thought she smelled at all, but understood why she said that, because I had felt dirty throughout the day—it had been maybe 75 degrees, and we'd been outside most of the day—and appreciated and felt a little surprised by her concern. It made me feel like we could be amenable to each other in some kind of "long-term thing."

We left the bus. She said something indicating she was going to sleep. I said I would walk her to her car. I didn't want her to leave. For some reason my main thought, again, walking with her toward her car, was that I wanted to sit closely with her in a low-lit restaurant. I felt depressed and somewhat confused that she wanted to leave. She said "I had fun" or something like that on the way to her car while smiling. I asked if she wanted to eat with me. She seemed to hesitate, then said she did. I felt depressed she hesitated but glad she wanted to eat with me. After maybe ten seconds she said she shouldn't, and wanted to sleep, or something, and we hugged at her car, and she asked if I needed a ride. I pointed at a sushi restaurant across the street. I said I was going there. She had a serious facial expression. We said "bye." She went in her car. I walked to the sushi restaurant feeling confused while sort of fantasizing that she would drive back—and also weakly thinking of possible reasons why she left.

This Message Has Been Discarded

Melissa Gira Grant

BEFORE WE FELL ASLEEP, he destroyed most of the photos. "I don't think I can give you what you want," he said when I'd come over. It was the third or fourth sentence we exchanged that night, after I commented on my coat, and he mentioned the heat, and in the dark I saw his camera on the floor and wondered if he had been with another woman before I arrived, and I didn't want to show that it mattered and I didn't ask, and he stepped into me and said, "I don't know that I can give you what you want," and picked up the camera.

We meant to get drunk, and we forgot. The air smelled like the end of summer, all clashing sour streets and overripe sweet, a little cashmere where I prematurely put on a sweater. I didn't bring a bottle of vodka. I kept my skirt on and I stepped out of my underwear, maybe because he asked me to. He often asked. I closed my eyes and found his wall with my hands and curved my spine toward him in both directions. My back moved more into his hand as the flash went and went. I kept my face turned away. I knew the photos would be horrible, and I spread my legs wider and I didn't know what I wanted and wasn't getting and then the flash stopped, and the sudden dark brought me back. He was hard for the first time since I walked in and he was turning my body from the waist around his hips and then over and down to the floor. *I'm here*, I said, or tried to say with my mouth, but instead I bowed and spread my cunt across his forearm.

He tilted my chin up to his face with his thumb and forefinger and he slid them forward and opened my mouth for me with his hand, and with his other hand he went between my legs, and smeared that wet across my cheeks and mouth. Our bodies were wet and quiet until he would strike me and I would fill his room. We filled so little of his room with our talk. We didn't know each other. We knew how to find this.

In the mornings, I would watch him weigh himself. I would feel him harden in my hand. I could see his kitchen and hear his streets fill and empty overnight. He told me when his cleaning lady was coming and offered me her email address, but he wouldn't eat in front of me. All he would want when we would wake up with the sheets rolled to the end of the bed would be to be inside me. I would have to say no only because he would always leave the room to put on a condom and neither of us would want to interrupt the other.

He laid his palm back the long way over my nose and the bones under my eyes, and my breath slowed to a hum. What I had come here for was all heat, breasts, and sweat, the drop in my gut I'd get when his hand moved too far from my body, signaling that his hand was about to come down on me. The pang for that empty space to close—that attuning myself to absence, all that I learned as a way to prepare myself for the force of his touch may have been why, when I shot out an arm and my legs pushed the other way against him and I came with the force of the length of my body, I still paused to consider the glass of water I heard tumble over, because I knew the camera had been as close to it as we were. It may have been how I trained my body to arouse itself at the prospect of loss.

I knew where he wasn't and then he turned my face to the side and I started to let myself love him once he made me look up and look for a long time. He reached around me, held my lip with his fingers, pressed my jaws apart. He said, "Look at me." He held my gaze hard, and I imagined that as I looked loving him, he stared back, evaluating me not as one to fuck but something else he hadn't let me inhabit yet. Maybe he didn't know what that was. We were both dreaming it. We both could go there alone and now, for a little bit, we didn't have to.

We turned over slow together and he hadn't come, and I found a place on his chest and someone started to talk. Then eventually he said something that made me say what had just become true, "You have to tell her," and we fucked again some but more tenderly.

"We don't talk about her," I said. It was the day that was the first time he kissed me in daylight, after he told me he was going back to see her. We hadn't seen each other in a little bit and so I came prepared for this to be over. We sat away from the sun and shared three glasses of wine in the window of a café. "What's going to happen?" I asked. I said her name. It was Sunday, and we hadn't woken up together and I had gotten out of bed alone.

"Being with you," he said, "you're the first time since" and he said her name for the first time in the present tense for the first time since the first night he kissed me, that night he asked me to meet him at a bar too close to his apartment and I chose a seat in the farthest back and told myself I didn't actually know what he wanted. When he arrived he folded his body in two beside me and after not much longer, with his eyes to the floor, he said her name and where she lived and how long they had been together and I wasn't prepared but I wasn't surprised when he kissed me, just like someone I wish he'd be, pulling me over his leg on the bench, onto him and I opened my legs as much as my skirt would allow and then further and let it ride over my waist. I shut my eyes, and I bit his lip.

The second time he said her name, we were quiet. I asked, "Why me?"

"With you," he said, looking past me, "I thought I would not regret it."

"And now?" I softened my jaw and my eyes without knowing what he meant when he said what he said next.

"Now, I don't want any secrets."

But that night in his bed what he said was, "I feel like I am getting away with something," and the minute-old memory of it made me cold, and the room began to recede behind my eyes, and became red, and I could see the road outside like it was in there with us. I could see the traffic lights hanging and they shifted in the dark and the breeze. They could hold a bit of our talking while we could look at each other and go quiet and wonder who goes first. I would pull the white cowl neck of my sweater aside and put my hands on the places between my neck and my breasts that were purple and gray and dotted with blood just under the skin. I would show him. They hurt to the touch. I would love them.

I would leave there as I always had, a black mark on my shirt from his floor, my come on his shirt, his come smeared and rubbed into my breasts at three in the morning, and a fine dark blue bruise on my ass and a grid of fingernail scratches and fuck, he made me come the last time by teething at my nipples as I stroked his cock between my legs, and he said he wanted me, and when I asked where, he said all around him. He pushed me ass up onto the bed, turned me over and said, hand on my throat, "Are we even now?"

And I said yes.

"And what do you want? Tell me."

"I'm scared to ask for more," I said.

"Tell me."

"I want you to fuck me."

It's so simple, and it's not true to say I never had to tell him what I wanted, that we only understood each other then by accident, that it was one I didn't mind.

We coiled tight against each other, and he wrapped his hands and held me and my cunt was filled with him and my ass and he played my body over, hard, breathless, all arms and chest and belly pressed down and back broke and I pulsed hard around his hands and screamed out, and said his name low and small, and when I thought I was done, again, his hands were holding me around the back to him, my cunt arched up to meet him, and I came and came, flooding us both from hip to hip. He cried out as he came over my chest, couldn't take my hand on his chest and he looked down at me, and he was there, just kneeling over me tall, like a gift.

Before I'm gone, I'm retelling the fuck to myself in my head. I start writing and I delete it. I start writing and I delete it. I start writing and I delete it and I write here instead: his hand was holding my neck down and his other was holding the camera up. It's a terrible image. It hurts and it's what I want and later it's what I'll return to most. I know this as it's happening. I find his eyes and I tell myself, *Miss this*. My cunt clutches up as the pressure keeps coming down on my throat and the light never stops filling my eyes and without him asking, I keep them open. Then I leave my body behind in the picture, which hardly existed, and now doesn't, and now does again because I am telling you. I see it now, but only because I am telling the story of it, and the image leaves me as I do, and the hands that held it.

I rose up from the bed, lifted the camera away from the pool of water, offered it to him without looking, and then we slept.

Contributors

Jonathan Ames is the author of *I Pass Like Night*; *The Extra Man*; *What's Not to Love?*; *My Less Than Secret Life*; *Wake Up, Sir!*; *I Love You More Than You Know*; *The Alcoholic*; and *The Double Life Is Twice As Good*. He's the creator of the HBO® Original Series *Bored to Death* and has had two amateur boxing matches, fighting as "The Herring Wonder."

William Ball is a blogger, which is a nice way of saying "dilettante." He writes poetry, mostly and has a BA in Philosophy from Connecticut College. This is his first publication. You can find him at ekstasis.tumblr.com and variously around the Northeast.

K. Bridgeman is a west coast native currently residing in New York City. Their work has been published online and most recently in *Best Lesbian Erotica* 2010. K. is the co-editor of *Stalled*, an anthology of stories by gender non-conforming people about sex-segregated spaces, which is forthcoming in 2011.

Arielle Brousse works at a cozy literary nonprofit in Philadelphia where she gets to meet and support fearless writers of all kinds, who collectively inspired her to be brave enough to write about very personal moments and share them with the world. In her free time she enjoys post-ironic crafting, deconstructing music videos and television shows with a feminist eye, and spooning her cat.

Tyler Coates grew up in the Northern Neck of Virginia and currently lives in Chicago. He attended James Madison University. His writing has appeared on This

Recording, Idolator, and The Awl. His personal blog can be found at tylercoates.tumblr.com.

Gina de Vries is a widely-published writer and activist who lives and loves in San Francisco. At press time, recent university appearances include Harvard, recent publications include *Bound to Struggle: Where Kink and Radical Politics Meet* and *The Revolution Starts at Home: Confronting Intimate Violence Within Activist Communities*, recent performances include "Girl Talk: a cis & trans woman dialogue," and recent porn appearances include Doing It Ourselves: The Trans Women Porn Project. Find out more at ginadevries.com, and keep track of her on the daily at queershoulder.tumblr.com.

Maria Diaz is an extremely old student at Oberlin College. She has been vomiting parts of her life out onto the Internet since 1997. Besides occasionally having sex with herbivores, she is one of the founding editor of Vegansaurus. She's also written for BitchBuzz, Media Elites, This Recording and b5media. You can find her in the club, or at mariadiaz.org

Sarah Dopp is a poet who builds websites and raises armies. Sometimes the poems look like websites, sometimes the websites look like armies, and sometimes the armies look like poems. She's the founder of Genderfork.com, a messybeautiful community blog about living outside of gender norms, and co-host of San Francisco's Queer Open Mic. Whatever she's been building lately is at SarahDopp.com.

Stephen Elliott is the author of seven books, most recently *The Adderall Diaries*. He is also the founding editor of The Rumpus.net.

Matthew Gallaway is a writer who lives in Washington Heights (New York City) with his partner Stephen and their three cats, Dante, Zephyr and Elektra. His first novel is *The Metropolis Case*.

Alex Hoyt is a writer who lives in Brooklyn, though not on Hoyt Street.

Halle Kiefer is a writer and comedian born outside of Cleveland and currently living in Brooklyn. She writes for the Awl, performs improv with her team Blood Money and has a weekly video series with comedian Jess Burkle. Read her insane ramblings at mustanghalle.tumblr.com.

Matthew Lawrence is a writer and former rentbear from Providence, Rhode Island. His blog, Mixtapes For Hookers, was originally designed for in-call escorts to time their sessions. Now he uses it mainly to complain and waste time.

Tao Lin (b. 1983) is the author of six books of fiction and poetry. His second novel, *Richard Yates*, will be published September 07, 2010 by Melville House. He has a blog.

Tess Lynch is a writer and actor originally from New York, currently living in Los Angeles. You can find more of her essays on her blog, Wipe Your Feet. That's it.

Erica Moore has 11 years of political and non-profit writing experience, none of which she employs in her second-person nocturnal ramblings on beenthinking.tumblr.com. When she is not writing, she is busy accumulating the 68 remaining passport stamps she needs to join the Travelers Century Club.

Peter Raffel is a high school student known for his blog at ohmeohyou.tumblr.com. He lives outside of Chicago with his family. He has a B in English.

Audacia Ray is a New York-based media maker and activist who is passionate about sexual rights. She hosts the monthly storytelling series The Red Umbrella Diaries and is the author of *Naked on the Internet: Hookups, Downloads, and Cashing In On Internet Sexploration*. She has also been an adjunct professor of sexuality at Rutgers University and the award-winning director and producer of the porn film *The Bi Apple*. Find out more about her many projects on WakingVixen.com, where she has blogged since 2004.

Charlotte Shane is a prostitute living on the East Coast. She is honored by the inexplicable popularity of her tumblr, Nightmare Brunette, which persists in spite of her liberal posting of Indian music and spiritual quotes.

Diana Vilibert has already said too much. She is a freelance writer in New York. You can find her at diana-vilibert.com.

Danny Vitolo grew up in small town upstate New York and has been writing about sex on the Internet for more than half his life. He's been living the big city life for a few years and is liking it just fine. He remembers trees fondly.

Douglas Wolk gets entertained for a living, has written a couple of books, and maintains a few too many blogs. He lives in Portland, Oregon.

About the book

Jez Burrows (jezburrows.com) is a designer and illustrator living and working in Edinburgh, UK. He is co-founder of independent press Sing Statistics, and his clients include *The New York Times*, *WIRED*, *GOOD*, *Dwell* and *Monocle*.

Nikola Tamindzic (ilovenikola.com), acclaimed New York portrait and fashion photographer, established his reputation as Gawker's house photographer in 2004 (and hasn't stopped shooting since). His work has been the subject of feature articles in *New York Times*, *PHOTO*, and *The British Journal of Photography*. He's been named Photographer of the Year in *Village Voice* (2007) and *L* magazine (2008), and Photographer of the Month in Paris *PHOTO* (October 2008). His clients include H&M, *NYLON*, *New York* magazine, *New Yorker*, *The Guardian*, *Village Voice*, *Time Out*, *Out*, *Maxim*, *Stuff*, and *The Sunday Times*. As of 2010, he's a regular contributor to *Vogue*.

About the editors

Melissa Gira Grant enjoys blogs and bloggers. She's written about sex and the Internet for Slate, The Frisky, *$pread* magazine, and Valleywag, and has contributed to the anthologies *Dirty Girls*, *Best Sex Writing*, and *Girl Crush*. She has an apartment in Brooklyn; her typewriter is in San Francisco.

Meaghan O'Connell moved to New York four years ago to be a live-in nanny. Since then she has interned at 826NYC, learned the Internet as Jonathan Coulton's assistant, written in coffee shops all over Brooklyn, and started a blog on Tumblr, where she now works as the Director of Outreach. This is her first publication.

Meaghan and Melissa know each other because of the Internet. In 2008, over blog posts and emails, they decided to make a book called *Coming & Crying*. When they met for the first time in New York a few months later, they immediately began making lists. They also discovered just how short they really are. With the support of six hundred and fifty one backers, they founded Glass Houses Press together in 2010. Though they now live on the same train line, they still finished writing this over gchat.

Acknowledgments

Coming & Crying would absolutely not be possible without the talents and support of a generous cadre of friends and fellow travelers, and to name those whose names still echo in our brains even this late in the game of writing this all out, here goes:

Our house photographer, and by way of that, a first witness and peerless collaborator, Nikola Tamindzic; the indomitable Cindy Gallop, for being fan-bloody-tastic and pushing us forward in all things ladybiz; Jez Burrows, for a love of the ampersand; Carlo de Jesus, whose talent took us beyond our own expectation; Halle Kiefer, Will McGinn, Kelsey Keith, Ashley Gates, Chris Hall and Lindsay Buehler, for always showing up; Sarah Hromack, for everything, sister; Samia Saleem, who is our own personal Pink Room; Nancy Schwartzman, for demanding nothing but realness; Tillie's Café, for your funny old men and your soundtrack and your coffee; Susan Barnett, whose patience and sense of humor helped us establish a house style for blowjob and who, as our very first reader, assured us that this thing we had was good; Swayspace, for sharing their Nina Simone and old letterpresses on a hard day that reminded us why we were doing this; Yancey and Perry and all of Kickstarter, for spending every day making a thing that helped us make a thing; Katie Roiphe, for shots fired; Anaïs Nin, for subway reading; Joan Didion, for cutting a bitch; Tumblr and Third Wave Foundation, for the stability to really do this, and who understood, and who tolerated working with us every day on little sleep, and who taught us to really go for it wherever we could; Hendrick's Gin, for our best mistakes to make; Jen Snow, for being basically amazing; Matt Langer, for the emoticons; Jay Wood, for staying up late; for the song and the answer, Leadbelly;

And for their humbling generosity, Erin O'Connell, Deirdre Benson, Michael Handler, Arielle Brousse, Andrew Krucoff, Leah Friedman, Kathryn Ratcliffe-Lee, Ben Millen, Cory Silverberg, Andrea O'Connell, James Turnbull, Dave Morin, Joel Martin, Tom Flaherty, Carlos Del Rio, Sara Pena Heick, Jeffery Guarino, Charlie O'Donnell, Joshua Allen, Ben Powell, Norman Council, Joy Jerome, Erica Ulstrom, Will Hutson, Jeffrey Grand, James McKay, Balthazar, David Karp, and John Maloney;

And also for all people everywhere who like sex and have feelings.

Coming & Crying is set in the typeface Dolly (by Underware.nl) and was printed and bound in Iceland by Oddi, on Munken Print White 100g.